ERIC GILL
The Inscriptions

Eric Gill's winning design, in the National Competition for Art Schools,
for a card plate to be made in pottery, 1900.

ERIC GILL
The Inscriptions

A descriptive catalogue

David Peace

Based on *The Inscriptional Work of Eric Gill*
An Inventory by Evan R. Gill

The Herbert Press

First published in Great Britain 1994
by The Herbert Press Ltd, 46 Northchurch Road, London N1 4EJ

House editor: Julia MacKenzie
Designed by Pauline Harrison

Set in Joanna
by Nene Phototypesetters Ltd, Northampton
Printed and bound in Great Britain by The Bath Press, Avon

A CIP catalogue record for this book is available
from the British Library.

ISBN 1-871569-66-4

Contents

For Rachel and Juliet

Preface

This new book could not easily have been made without *The Inscriptional Work of Eric Gill: An Inventory* by Evan R. Gill, to which in a small way I contributed, and I am grateful for the authority of Evan Gill's family to use it. It is the foundation on which I have built.

To compile his book Evan Gill used his brother's diaries and notebooks, and the rubbings and drawings that I have also examined in the St Bride Printing Library in London. Evan Gill's Preface has been retained because it contains much relevant information.

The 1964 *Inventory* had 808 items. Several were known to have been destroyed in wartime bombing or lost, but were included because drawings or rubbings had survived and could still be studied. Even now the location of many items remains unknown. Some forty years of searching and photographing have, however, produced much new information which extends as well as amends the original book. As a result, this catalogue covers 891 items, or 964 if individual examples are included within a single reference number. In addition, there are eighteen unidentified rubbings in the St Bride Printing Library on which Evan Gill did not find enough evidence of date or associations to include in his *Inventory* (see Appendix VIII).

NUMBERING AND ATTRIBUTION OF JOBS

Despite the need to add to, and in some cases to amend, Evan Gill's list, I decided to keep his numbering so that the *Inventory* and this descriptive catalogue can go together for reference. Newly discovered items, or those in my opinion safely attributable to Eric Gill, have '/P' added to the catalogue number. Unidentified examples are numbered U1–U18 in Appendix VIII. Some items have been destroyed, but these are included in the catalogue and the indexes.

A list of apprentices, pupils and assistants can be referred to in Appendix I, but I have not repeated the note in each entry on who cut the lettering. As explained in Evan Gill's Preface, jobs were formally attributed to the workshop, not to the carver. Before 1906, when Joseph Cribb joined him as his first apprentice, all lettering may be attributed to Eric Gill. I have, however, shown where it is clear after 1906 that Eric himself carved the lettering. Signed examples are rare, e.g. The Ten Commandments pen-drawn on oak (46) at Charwelton, the Lawley memorial at Escrick (96), the Ravenhill memorial at Canterbury (135) and the Victoria and Albert Museum war memorial (365). (The fine lettering on the war memorial at Emmanuel College, Cambridge, signed 'E.G.' is by Ernest Gillick.)

LOCATIONS

At least 170 sites are still undiscovered. The locations of many items listed in the *Inventory* were incorrect, because of scanty or misleading evidence at the time. These have been corrected where known.

A list of locations by counties and countries, to help those who wish to make exploratory tours, is provided as Appendix II.

SIZES

Overall sizes of memorials are given where known. Sizes of inscriptions are in inches, ignoring fractions. Sizes of rubbings (which do not show overall sizes) are prefaced by 'R'.

DATING

The year of production or fixing is given as accurately as possible. In the early years the month is given to indicate gradual development.

STARRED ITEMS

The inscriptions which I think merit a special visit or study, having seen them, are asterisked. These personal choices depend on a variety of reasons; there is no easy 'points system' for their inclusion. In Sir John Betjeman's words, many of the starred items are the ones I would 'cycle twelve miles against the wind to see'. The interest of other items, unstarred, may be assessed from the descriptions; items yet undiscovered may be very special.

QUOTATIONS

Whereas the *Inventory* included some brief quotations, and an index for reference, I have preferred to quote many, and more fully, in the text. The commemorative words in Eric Gill's memorials are often so unusual and evocative as to show he had special flair, not only for monumental inscriptions but – something rather different – choice of words on monuments.

ARCHITECTS

Architects' names are included where known. Most of them were members (as was Eric Gill from 1904 to 1909) of the Art Workers Guild, e.g. W. D. Caröe, Edward Prior, Beresford Pite, Charles Holden and Sir Edwin Lutyens.

SPECIAL ASPECTS

Appendix IV lists the heraldry associated with the inscriptions. Other appendices deal with less well-known aspects of his work on seals, medals, coinage, stamps and his thirty-eight war memorials, only a few of which are well known.

FURTHER DISCOVERIES

It is hoped that where locations are unknown the details quoted here may lead to the discovery of the sites. The Index of Persons and Institutions may be particularly helpful in this.

Inevitably there will be omissions and errors in a catalogue of this nature. Circumstances and advancing years have precluded my examining records in collections in the United States. If any reader discovers new information please send it to the publisher.

ILLUSTRATIONS

The aim has been to illustrate the great range of Eric Gill's work, with special attention to early examples and others never before illustrated. In gathering together the illustrations there have been certain difficulties: many of the inscriptions in the open air are now so weathered that a photograph does not show very much; those in buildings are often not well lit. I have some reluctance in illustrating rubbings since they do not show the use of colour or gilding, or the surrounding mouldings.

With opportunities denied to Evan Gill, I have continued his work published thirty years ago; and the resulting catalogue is the conclusion of some forty years' investigations on my part. My contribution is a measure of my regard for Eric Gill's work, and a tribute to the memory of Evan Gill as a friend.

Acknowledgements

First of all I am grateful to Evan Gill's family for authority to use the original Inventory.

Numerous people have assisted me with my work and I would particularly like to thank the following: James Mosley at the St Bride Printing Library in London for enabling me to examine the records there; Sean Hawkins, whose researches leading to the discovery of locations have been invaluable, and the Revd Michael Staines, John Skelton and Joe Cribb who also provided information on this matter; Meg Davies for the indexing; John Dreyfus for regular advice and encouragement over thirty years; and notably John Keatley and the Keatley Trust for help towards the costs of compiling the catalogue; Polly Pitt and Lynn White who deciphered my notes and typed numerous scripts; and to my publisher for advice and much patience.

DAVID PEACE
Hemingford Abbots
Cambridgeshire
1994

Illustrations: Acknowledgements

Numbers refer to plates.

The Studio: Frontispiece; The Principal, Cheltenham Ladies College 23; City of York 26; Victoria & Albert Museum 30, 44; Westminster Cathedral 33, 34; Sean Hawkins 37, 46; The Headmaster, Royal Russell School 40; John Skelton 47; St Bride Printing Library 39, 41, 48, 49, 52, 56, 62, 68, 70; Cotham Parochial Church Council (photograph: John Christopher) 43; *Good Work* (Catholic Art Association, USA) 50; Worshipful Company of Goldsmiths 57, 58; *Sculptured Memorials & Headstones* 60; Edward Leigh (photographer) 67; Deputy Master of the Royal Mint 69; National Postal Museum 72, 73.

Kate Guy for drawings from rubbings by the author 3, 16, 24, 25; rubbings by the author 9, 10, 13, 35, 66; drawings by the author 4, 8, 12, 15, 20, 21, 29, 61, 71.

Other photographs, and the vignettes in the text, are by the author.

Preface by Evan R. Gill

to The Inscriptional Work of Eric Gill: An Inventory (1964)

Lettering in history exhibits diverse forms and mediums. The attempt is here made to record the inscriptional work, whether incised into stone, painted upon wood or engraved in metal, by one of the most copious executants of the art known in our time: Eric Gill.

Let it be said at the outset that this record is not complete and, further, that the treatment of the entries is not uniform. This is inevitable for reasons which I shall try to make clear. Then too, what has been recorded was not always wholly the work of one man's hands. First let me speak of the questions of completeness and uniformity.

SOURCES

Though Eric Gill was in important respects the most methodical of men, his eye, more particularly at the outset of his career as a letter-cutter, was directed more closely to the job in hand rather than to its recording in a catalogue, for the benefit of himself or any other who should come after. Rather, the job itself was its own record. This is not to imply that he kept no records of work done. We have his personal diaries (kept most meticulously), one or two notebooks and, most valuable of all an 'exercise' book entitled List of Jobs. This was begun in 1902 and carries us to the end of 1909.

Earlier than the diaries or the notebooks, as sources of information for E.G.'s inscriptional work, are the two Statements of Account he rendered to W. D. Caröe, architect to the Ecclesiastical Commissioners, in whose drawing office he worked (somewhat unhappily) for the three years 1900–2. Both sources relate to work done for Caröe in 1901. They are of such paramount interest that it is worthwhile placing them on record. The earlier of the two (from his lodgings at 68 Victoria Road [now Victoria Rise], Clapham) is for the following jobs:

	hrs.
Clapton – Foundation stone, June 21–25	8¾
Canterbury Chapel – Dedication stone, July 1–2	4½
„ „ (revised) July 10	2
Trinity Lodge, Cambridge, July 16	2½
„ „ & Cranbrook door, July 18–19	4¾
Total	22½

As his charges were based at the rate of 1s. per hour the bill amounted to £1 2s 6d!

Let us now return to the *List of Jobs*. This, unfortunately, with very few exceptions, proved of limited value in supplying us with the kind of detailed information we desired for the *Inventory*. The name of the person or institution commemorated and the location of the work are lacking. E.G. gives the number, name of client and a brief note of the work. That is all. An example will show what the record comprises.

122 Mr. Williams White. Memorial Tablet. Bognor.

Which being interpreted (cf. No. 66) means:

Memorial brass in St Wilfred's Church, Bognor, in memory of James Allen Freeborn Howell, 1887–1904, a pupil at a school of which Williams White was the headmaster.

It will now be appreciated why not every one of the inscriptional jobs is recorded here; and also why, for such as have been given, the entries are lacking in uniformity. For the rest – E.G.'s work done subsequent to 1909 – the compiler has had to rely (with one major exception) almost wholly on the diary entries; themselves cryptic, sketchy or ambiguous. The reader must remember that the diary entries were solely for E.G.'s own information.

We now come to the major exception referred to above. By way of introduction let me outline the procedure E.G. generally followed when approached with a commission. It was his general practice to submit to his client either a sketch or a finished drawing of the proposed memorial. This, if approved, would be returned to him. He would then prepare a full-scale drawing. A considerable number, though, as will be seen, by no means all, of the original sketches or drawings would find their way back to his client. Fortunately for us, however, E.G. retained a great many of these. Still more fortunately the Monotype Corporation was able to acquire from the Executors of the estate this collection of sketches and drawings, together with a very considerable number of rubbings of the finished works. Without these 'pieces' the present work could hardly have been compiled. The following figures will serve to illustrate the point.

Our Catalogue lists some 808 entries of 'Jobs Done'. Of these there are no less than 635 sketches or drawings in the Monotype collection which represent 376 distinct works – roughly 46 per cent of the total. It should be noted that these figures do not take the rubbings into account.

The descriptions of these jobs in the catalogue, it need hardly be emphasized, are of necessity compressed into a few lines, without regard to size, purpose or importance. Let me illustrate my point by referring the reader to the war memorial for New College (No. 398) which involved cutting no less than 270 2 in. and 5,060 1 in. capital letters! An extreme example, doubtless, but one which is not without significance.

ATTRIBUTION OF THE WORKS

An important question immediately poses itself. Is it possible to segregate the work of E.G.'s own hands, absolutely, from that of his assistants?[1] The answer must be 'No'. Nor would an attempt at such a segregation necessarily be desirable even if it were possible – for reasons which it is hoped to make convincing. No hard and fast line can be drawn between the inscriptions which came wholly and absolutely from his hands, or partly his and those of his assistants, or were interpreted either in whole or in part by one or more of his assistants. This aspect of his work as sculptor or letter-cutter and his attitude towards the principles involved was admirably treated by his very close friend the late Father Desmond Chute in a study of E.G.'s work as yet unpublished.[2] I am grateful for permission to quote from it:

'On Ditchling Common, at Capel-y-ffin or wherever Gill set up shop, life was lived on this [a small workshop manned by a group no larger than a family] model in a passion of shared work and ideas. Work did not end where leisure began, for leisure was but another kind of work. Everything made there was wholly inspired and entirely due to him. This does not necessarily mean that all works came wholly from his hand. For if in a period when sculptors' use of the pointing machine was taken for granted, he was adamant against this or other devices that rob men of responsibility, on the other hand he made ample use of the collaboration of fellow stone-cutters, esteeming this a mutual benefit. Nor did he hesitate to set his name to work thus produced – metaphorically in most cases, for he did not hold with signed work.

'Whereas then in one sense everything shown in this book is his, in another few are the works which owe nothing to his assistants, while fewer still proceed from the master's hand alone.[3] One or two (e.g. Nos. 330–1 and 342) are definitely *bottega* works cut wholly by apprentices or pupils. Their inclusion is deliberate as illustrating the workshop system itself and his conception of it, and because it is what Eric would have wished.

'To anyone who has learnt a craft in a workshop the elaborate *expertise* whose aim is to spot the master's hand, isolating his work from that of the school, is simply laughable. The touches of the master are as fleeting as they are frequent whereas the imprint of his mind is everywhere and not least in what he has least touched.

'At times someone would happen to single out an inscription and Eric would say "I'm glad you like that: Albert (or Laurie or Denis) cut it". He no more sought to conceal the fact than it would have occurred to him to show or sell the stone under the assistant's name, so long as he was such. In the workshop anonymity stands for distinction not privation. There was no shortage of outstanding masons in the Middle Ages: that is why they ceased to stand out. Besides, anonymity is more than namelessness, not just an historical accident but a peculiar positive quality. In Gill's own words, "If every single mediaeval carving were signed and not a single modern one, it would still be true that medieval art is 'anonymous' and modern art isn't". But his was. And so was that of his pupils.'

As to Fr Chute's reference to 'signed' work, so rarely did Eric 'sign' his work that it may be of interest to draw attention to three exceptions to his general rule. These are the Lawley monument in Escrick church (No. 96) erected in 1906, the large war memorial for the staff of the V & A Museum, South Kensington (No. 365) erected in 1919 and the Hamersley tablet of 1930 at Rycote, near Thame (No. 542). The second

---

[1] Gill's first apprentice, Joseph Cribb, came to him in June 1906. All the works therefore from 1901 to that date may rightly be regarded as wholly the work of Gill's hands.

[2] [The book was never published although the unfinished preface appeared in *Good Work*, Vol. XXVII, no. I, Winter 1964 – Ed.]

[3] The reader must be told that Fr Chute's study was concerned primarily with sculptures.

of these carries, too, the 'signature' of Joseph Cribb who, happy to relate, after fifty-five years at the game is still carving a niche for himself and the craft of letter-cutting in Ditchling, whither he migrated in 1907 with his master from London.[4]

Let me, please, here pay tribute in my personal capacity to all those 'chaps' (Eric's word for them) who so faithfully served him indoors and out-of-doors, in all weathers, in good times and bad, at some time or other between the years from 1906 to 1940, the year of his death. The least I can do is record their names as I have done in an Appendix to this catalogue.

It is necessary to add that as a matter of course Joseph Cribb and the other chaps who assisted in the execution of the inscriptional commissions that came into the workshop, were all masters of the letter forms which had earlier, under Eric Gill's sole hand, evolved into that fully developed and perfected style which is his own individual and, it has been said by a competent judge, 'immortal' contribution to the lapidary art.

A record of this kind owes much to relatives of the persons commemorated, to incumbents of parishes and to officials of institutions with whom I have corresponded. Their replies have been uniformly helpful; several letters concerning memorials in church and public institutions have revealed a heart-warming interest and pleasure in learning, for the first time, who was responsible for the design and execution of the memorials in their care.

My correspondents are far too numerous to mention by name but I here express my gratitude to them and, in particular, to officials of two libraries in which I have worked – the Guildhall in London, and the Picton in Liverpool; also to the following whose help was very considerable – the late Mrs Eric Gill, her daughter Mrs René Hague, her son-in-law Mr Denis Tegetmeier, my brother Major V. K. Gill, also Mr David Peace, ARIBA, MTPI, Mr Stanley Scott, Mr Walter Shewring and Mr Roger Smith.

In conclusion I acknowledge my indebtedness to the Monotype Corporation for having facilitated my progress through the maze of material in Monotype House and for the assistance given me by various members of their staff, above all to Mr John Dreyfus for the guidance and advice he gave me so frequently, patiently and ungrudgingly.

E.R.G.
LIVERPOOL 1963

---

[4] [Joseph Cribb died in 1967 – Ed.]

Introduction: Forty Years of Lettering

I first met Eric Gill in 1934 at the exhibition of the Design and Industries Association in London. It was here that he exhibited his own tombstone MEMENTO MEI E.G. LAPIDARII predicting his death in 1936 – happily he survived till 1940. He was kind to me, and gave me good advice about a wood-engraving I had done (which incorporated his Perpetua roman capitals), notably that I had not used the tool to its best advantage. We met again twice, and corresponded – about architecture. But the bond was already established in 1928, while I was at school, where I was first captivated by his roman alphabet. A print of this, published by the Victoria and Albert Museum, was pinned to the door of the store cupboard in the art room, and in this way I was nourished by Gill's lettering for four years.

Fifteen years after Eric Gill's death I heard that an inventory was being prepared by his brother Evan, a statistician, who was happily employed in retirement on his brother's works. Somehow I became involved in helping to compile the *Inventory*. Owing to a war wound from about 1917, Evan was unable to drive a car; but there was I, living in the Midlands, mobile, and keen to help in tracking down the locations of Eric Gill's inscriptions from scraps of evidence provided by Evan. So, when *The Inscriptional Work of Eric Gill: An Inventory* was published in 1964, I treasured what Evan wrote in the copy he gave me: 'For David Peace, an aide who never decamped.' After Evan's death, in continuation of his work, and following further explorations, I wrote the *Addenda and Corrigenda* to the *Inventory*, which was published in America in 1972. My investigations have continued since then, so for about forty years I have been finding and photographing the inscriptions all over England and Wales. Scotland is still unexplored; and there are many works, the whereabouts of which are still unknown. The time then came to record all my discoveries, at least to help others to find and enjoy the widely distributed works. At this stage, my friend John Keatley made what appeared to be a casual suggestion that I should do a catalogue raisonné of the inscriptions; then he added that the Keatley Trust, committed to twentieth-century art, would provide funds for the further exploratory work needed.

The *Inventory* entries finishing at number 762 covered 808 inscriptions. But many items had been lost through wartime bombing or other demolitions; and in many cases the locations were unknown. This is still so, though the present catalogue has more information than the original. It also has my own descriptions and comments, having been concerned with the design of lettered inscriptions for many years.

This catalogue describes nearly a thousand individual lettering jobs, done between 1901 and 1940. While Gill's roman letters are famous, less well known is the range of materials he used: stone, marble, cast bronze, engraved brass, painted wood, pen-drawn letters written direct on oak, and even sheet copper by the method known as repoussé (letters beaten in reverse on the underside, to provide high relief and reflected highlights). In all of these methods he carefully respected the material and knew its limitations.

RANGE OF MATERIALS

From 1901 the jobs included memorials, foundation stones, sundials, even clock faces, paper weights, and garden rollers with words on the ends.

In many of these jobs, especially in the early years before 1906, when Joseph Cribb joined him as an apprentice, there are unexpected flourishes and letters joined together – and not only where this was needed in a line just to get the spacing right. There is often a sense of fun, as if Gill was throwing his hat in the air and saying, 'There is nothing I like so much as doing lettering'.

More seriously, he took great care to integrate work into its setting, whether it was a war memorial in a town, or a wall tablet in a church. Tablets were usually fixed flush with the wall surfaces, not projecting on corbels; thus they became not so much an addition but part of the structure. You can tap the stone and it rings, like a tightly stretched drum.

There is much variety in his inscriptions. Often the size of letters in a single job changes from roman caps and lower case to italic; and red and blue and gilding are used, especially where there is little light.

AN EARLY SUCCESS

Already at the age of eighteen Gill was designing lettering in the style of 'art nouveau' which, after teaching by Edward Johnston, he was keen to disown – taking over for a time Johnston's own class. His first published design, with which in 1900 he won the National Competition for Art Schools, was prophetic, since it contained the seeds of much that was to come (frontispiece).

His design, submitted from Chichester, was for a 'card plate' to be carried out in pottery. The decoration was to be in 'sgraffito', even an early indication of future engravings. In the centre, the word 'Cards' is within a ribboned surround, the 'C' and 'A' being incorporated as one. On the rim, runs a text – 'Fresh as the first beam flickering on a sail that brings our friends up from the underworld'; this shows his love of apt inscriptions to suit the occasion – in this case to hold visiting cards, a customary need then in polite society. Integrating lettering and site, and free in letter form, it breathes the kind of liveliness which invigorated Gill's work for the next forty years.

The influence of Edward Johnston on Eric Gill cannot be exaggerated. Gill's approach to the layout of inscriptions, his early calligraphic letter forms, his knowledge of roman capitals all stem from Johnston – whose knowledge in turn stemmed from his study of the historic roots of letter forms, including Hübner's examples of the first and second centuries. The great influence on Johnston and Gill, and their attitude to design, was W. R. Lethaby, the architect, Head of the L.C.C.

Central School of Arts and Crafts, of whom Gill wrote: 'Who shall measure the greatness of this man – one of the few men of the nineteenth century whose minds were enlightened directly by the Holy Spirit?'

HISTORIC ROOTS

Similarly, the influence on Gill of two years as an articled pupil in the office of the architect W. D. Caröe has seldom been recognized; it was reflected in his flair for responding to an architectural setting, and in his own excellent draughtsmanship. His details of mouldings are exceptional.

A favourite letter form in Caröe's office was 'Lombardic': but the architect's affection for this style was not shared by his pupil. Though Gill was obliged to use it on a memorial after he had left the practice, he noted on the drawing, 'This was done under compulsion'. Even so, Gill's treatment of it had touches of great ingenuity and beauty. In many such notes on the drawings the man comes alive.

While a study of his lettering could also include his engravings, from simple bookplates to the enrichment of books, these are not strictly inscriptions. But this catalogue gives an opportunity to record Gill's inscriptional work in his designs for postage stamps, and for coinage, seals and medals, all of which involved lettering.

Yet another side of Gill's genius comes to the fore in his work on memorials – his designs for heraldry. In this he showed his knowledge of the medieval origins of this art – the need to have bold silhouettes of charges, leading to rapid identification.

Part of the difficulty in assessing the authentic work by Gill is that he rarely signed it. The clue to his own authorship is a small cross with square dots in each quarter; occasionally he replaced the dots with his initials, A.E.R.G. A rare signature is on the old Cavendish site in the centre of Cambridge on the former Mond Laboratory. In the brickwork is carved a large crocodile, and a calligraphic monogram of E.G. is 'V'-cut to form its tongue – a typical bit of fun (582A/P).

Deriving from Gill's reputation for fine lettering done in Caröe's office (and even though he resigned somewhat precipitately, the links between architect and carver were well established) Caröe gave him a number of commissions – foundation stones, and work in bronze and copper. Caröe, like Johnston, was a member of the Art Workers Guild and through the Guild commissions came from architects such as Beresford Pite, Harrison Townsend, and Edward Prior – who first commissioned Gill to carve bold lettering and a long inscription on a building in Cambridge in 1903 – and later from Charles Holden and Lutyens. A little work came from Herbert Baker, Aston Webb, Morley Horder, Hubert Worthington and Edward Maufe, whose commissions embraced sculpture and lettering right up to the time of Gill's death.

In inscriptional work outside architecture, Gill's association with the Art Workers continued in the collaboration with George Friend, the metal engraver.

Gill was elected to the Art Workers Guild in 1904 as 'letter cutter and sign writer', though by 1909 he found himself out of sympathy with the arts and crafts movement as embodied in the Guild, and resigned. He is said to have felt it pandered to

the rich. But he was soon replaced in the Guild by his brother Macdonald Gill –
Max – who collaborated with him on a number of commissions.

WORDS

Understandably, Gill was closely concerned with memorials and gravestones. Very
many of them finish with a scriptural text, so aptly chosen as to lead one to believe
he commonly influenced the choice. He was after all the son and grandson of
clergymen. There is no doubt of his love of fine words. In compiling inscriptions,
the phrasing, line by line, was skilfully worked out, so readily do they run. Usually
placed at the foot of the commemorative words, one is led in fact to read them.

A few years before his conversion in 1913 to the Roman Catholic faith Gill cut
inscriptions in Latin. Later, he showed – as in his English – his care for the order of
Latin words. He wrote that an inscription 'reads more easily if it begins with an
accented first syllable' (comparing 'pácem' with 'oráte') and stressed the importance
of rhythms 'ending with the fullest cursus – oo.o/.' (535)

A final letter in a line will often be extended with a calligraphic stroke clearly
showing Johnston's influence, or with a flourish of Gill's own invention. Johnstonian touches appear in inscriptions on stone in the form, for example, of square
dots between words. More fundamentally, it is the influence of Johnston which
gave rise to Gill's freedom of approach to carved roman lettering, particularly in his
early days as a monumental mason. Especially in this early work there is a certain
disunity in the form of letters; it is rare, for example, to find consistent capital 'M's.
And in early work – perhaps deriving from a close study of the Trajan letter form –
he preferred a fairly sharp initial angle on the 'M'. Very often a capital 'R' – yet only
a rare 'K' – has the leg extended. The development of the 'R' is specially interesting.
(Fig. 8)

When business later became so brisk that a standard alphabet for the workshop
was necessary, Gill's recognizable roman capitals were more regularly perfect. Thus
some of their life was lost. Apprentices would be anxious that their work should be
correct. But the halo of perfection in letter form and symmetry of layout left the
work less human, less lively. For this, architects may have been to blame, wanting
foundation stones based on layouts on a centre line – what Gill called 'symmetrical'
arrangements as opposed to 'massed' layouts where the lines are close together and
about equal in length. 'Absolute equality is quite unnecessary.'

Most monumental masons will carefully centre an inscription, line after line, but
Gill seldom used such a layout for a whole design. In his work he centred or
dispensed with this idea even within a single tablet or gravestone. Part will be
centred, part will be 'justified' – or 'ranged left', leaving a ragged righthand edge.
This leads to a liveliness denied to centred texts – especially when, as he advised in
1903 in his section of Johnston's *Writing & Illuminating & Lettering*, capitals, small letters,
italics, red and blue, and gilding are all used in a single example. These contrasts led
to life and unity. As Johnston said, 'Freedom is an essential quality of all good
work'.

EARLY WORK

Of the greatest interest are the first hundred recorded examples of his work between 1901 and 1906, the period before Joseph Cribb joined him. Indeed, even the first twenty years of Gill's inscriptional work show a much greater variety than the later periods. By 1920 the workshop employed seven apprentices and assistants, due to the number of jobs. Moreover, Gill's growing fame meant he was undertaking a variety of activities – engraving, carving, type design, writing and lecturing – outside the field of letter-cutting, though he continued to prepare the layouts of inscriptions for the workshop.

The first hundred were done at a rate of about eighteen per year. They include numerous foundation stones and seven jobs involving direct carving on the stone walls of churches. Here is both assurance and a clear association with architecture. These early years also saw the first of his war memorials – two to those who died in the South African war – the first lettering for W. H. Smith's shop fascias, for which Gill's lettering was used until 1975; a dozen other examples of painted lettering, including a remarkable job at Christ Church, Brixton in association with Johnston; the series of copper panels at Charterhouse, full of interest in detail; and some forty wall tablets and grave memorials. Perhaps the most unexpected job to discover from this period is the inscribing of the Ten Commandments directly with a pen on to oak panels at Charwelton near Daventry (46), where in 1904 his friend G. C. Carter had rebuilt the chancel.

THE WORKSHOP

By 1905, Gill was designing initial letters for Count Kessler's Cranach Press in Germany. In that year he was appointed to teach 'monumental masonry and lettering' at Paddington College – two sessions per week at 12s 6d per session. The L.C.C. Education Committee minutes described his qualifications as 'Formerly a Council Artisan Scholar. Highly recommended by Mr Lethaby.' Gill's range of work is evident in the statement that 'the development of lettering for various purposes and materials, pen and brush, wood, stone and metal will be studied'. Kelly's Directory for Hammersmith of 1907–8, includes 'Gill and Christie' in a property on the west of Black Lion Lane. They were described as calligraphers as well as inscription carvers. (Lawrence Christie was another pupil of Johnston. The partnership with Gill ended in 1908.)

After Joseph Cribb joined him at the age of fifteen, Gill moved to Ditchling, keeping on the Hammersmith workshop for a time; and the amount of work doubled. In this period the first alphabets appeared, cut for the Victoria and Albert Museum in 1909. For a few years he was helped by his architect brother Max (Macdonald Gill), renowned in his own right for large decorative maps and murals. Substantial college work began at Oxford and Cambridge. Foundation stones of this time include the remarkable one (220) for the King Edward VII Galleries at the British Museum designed by Sir John Burnet – so good an example of integration with the grandeur of the façade that it can readily pass unnoticed.

Lettering jobs now ranged from the elaborately framed Wynne-Finch memorials in North Wales (75A/P and 122A/P) to the grand inscription on a 9-ft-high panel in Cheltenham Ladies College (132) and the triptychs at Thelwall and Shifnal (111 and 150A/P) in pen lettering raised with gesso and gilded. Memorials for the famous came his way, ranging in scope between the lettering on the graves of Oscar Wilde in Paris (255), Archbishop Frederick Temple at Canterbury (44) and Holman Hunt in St Paul's (211). Already in these early years Gill was the carver chosen to cut the title on the base of Rodin's 'Burghers of Calais' (299) and of the statue of Field-Marshal Wolseley in Westminster (376).

Outstanding in this early period – and in the whole of his career – were the fourteen Stations of the Cross, designed in 1913, for Westminster Cathedral (284), some with the lettering like a textured background. (Other Stations, less well known, were carved at Bradford, Leatherhead and Oxford.)

THE LATER YEARS

The years 1919–25 bring home the frightening loss of men in World War I. While the words and texts on individual wall tablets have a harrowing immediacy, the war memorial with its list of names, so much a feature of every town and village, has a message that can easily be lost. Outstanding in their impact and variety, Gill designed thirty-eight war memorials. For this his background in architectural drawing was a great help; and beside his feeling for the requirements of a building in fixing a tablet or cutting direct in the wall, he now showed his ability to respond to the requirements of a town site and surrounding roads.

Increasingly from 1924, sculpture and lettering are considered together. It was in this year he was invited to submit designs for new coinage, though these, unlike some of his work on postage stamps, were not carried out. The year 1924 was also the beginning of the great period of his wood engravings, in many of which lettering formed an important part, notably in *The Four Gospels*, published by the Golden Cockerel Press in 1935. In the same year he designed the vast bas-reliefs with interspersed lettering, commissioned by the British Government, for what is now the United Nations building in Geneva.

Between 1926 and 1940 the carved lettering jobs were turned out at about one every fortnight, including ten alphabets. Gill drew the layouts, but seldom cut the lettering. The jobs are credited to individual assistants in the *Inventory*.

While Gill's contribution to the history of lettering ended with his death in 1940, his influence continues in the work of his apprentices. In the imagination they have brought to bear in designing new letter forms and carving in a traditional way, the master lives on.

Having known and loved Gill's work since my school days, and having recorded the lettering for forty years, I hope this catalogue, with my descriptions, and echoing my enthusiasms, will lead others to enjoy more widely the astonishing breadth of Gill's contribution to the arts.

THE CATALOGUE

NUMBERING is as in the *Inventory*, with items discovered by the author, or in his view reasonably attributable to E.G., marked '/P'.

SIZES are in inches, ignoring fractions, unless otherwise stated.

RUBBINGS held in the St Bride Printing Library are marked 'R'.

ASTERISKS show the author's choice of specially important items.

1 Inscription on white marble: 'JANE LISTER a dear child.' Inspired by the wall tablet in Westminster Abbey Cloisters, which reads 'JANE LISTER dear childe died Oct 7 1688'. Though unsigned this is inscribed on reverse 'My first insct.'

> The illustration in the *Inventory* (Plate I) shows a floral infilling for a 'Q' and an unexpected floral tail for an italic 'l'. There is a generous 'D' (with a lift to the curve at the top) and long-legged 'R's. There is also a half-uncial 'd' and two kinds of small 'a'. It is probably a practice piece after tuition by Johnston. (The fish on the published rubbing is from another source.) Now in Kettle's Yard, Cambridge.
> 7 × 11; c.1902.

2 Stone tablet in Chichester Cathedral in memory of PERCY JOSEPH HISCOCK, 'five years a chorister and five years a bellringer of this Cathedral a volunteer in the Royal Sussex Regiment ... who fell at Retiefs Nek', died 1900, aged 21.

> The original drawing has a pencilled note 'A.E.R.G. 1901, before attending L.C.C. & before E.J.'s teaching.' Nine lines of turn-of-the-century caps.
> 9 × 20; 1901.

*3 Foundation stone of South African cloister of Charterhouse School, Godalming, Surrey: ABSENTES ADSVNT MDCCCCI; and a five-line inscription in Latin recording the laying of the foundation stone by Robert Baden-Powell: OPPIDI MAFEKING DEFENSOR INVICTUS.

> This stone, with raised lettering within incised panels, has lettering on three sides, being incorporated in a buttress. The architect was W. D. Caröe, the lettering Lombardic as was customary in his office. The treatment of this stone typifies E.G.'s own feeling for architecture, in which lettering is designed as an integral part of a building, rather than seeming an addition. August 1901.

*4 Foundation stone for St Michael's, Edmonton.

> Though No. 4 in the *Inventory*, this may well have been the very first architectural com-mission. It is also lettered on the inner face of the wall. Incorporating a rosette at the top, this ten-line inscription, centred, is in simple, scarcely seriffed roman caps, slightly sloping. It is characterized by several instances of unexpectedly small letters, and 'V's and an 'H' with the left stroke tucked under adjoining 'T's. The phrasing and silhouette of the inscrip-tion show an early regard for the solid, massed texture of words. Architect, W. D. Caröe.
> 27 × 18; August 1901.

1 Integration of lettering and architecture: the foundation stone in the buttress of the South African cloister at Charterhouse School, 1901 (3).

2 Detail of the foundation stone at Charterhouse, 1901 (3).

5 Inscription in memory of WILLIAM FRANCIS WILLIAMS, d.1858, also of
ROBERT HENRY WILLIAMS, d.1864 and FANNY EMILY SORRELL, d.1900.·

> This fine mature work within an architectural frame seems to be much later than the
> '1901' in the Inventory, probably cut in 1909. It is described later at No. 168.
> R 38 × 26.

6 Tombstone at Brookwood Cemetery, Surrey, in memory of JOHN
WINTERBOTHAM BATTEN, K.C. – 1831–1901. An inscription, in memory of
SARAH LANGSTAFFE BATTEN – 1835–1908, was added in 1909.

> A fine massed inscription of caps and lower-case roman; long legs for 'R' and 'K'.
> c. 20 × 27; c.1902. (See also 236)

7 Tombstone with inscription in French at Brookwood Cemetery (near No.6) in
memory of ALICE JUNOD, d.1902. 'Oui, la bonté et la gratuité me suiveront tous
les jours de ma vie et mon habitation sera dans la maison de l'Eternel pour de
longs jours.'

> The name in large caps, the rest nicely massed.
> c.15 × 20; May 1902.

7A/P Foundation stone for St Barnabas, Walthamstow. Architect, W.D.Caröe.

> Almost impossible to examine at floor level behind the wooden altar-table, the nine-line
> inscription is in roman caps of a sort, centred: art nouveau is in evidence. The phrasing,
> line by line, is carefully done, for the avoidance of punctuation, and states that 'This
> church ... is to be built at the cost of Richard Foster / A merchant of the City of London /
> as a thank offering to Almighty God / for numberless mercies during a long life / this
> stone ...' etc. There are long-legged 'R's and small 'o's, 'p's which go below the line, and
> an occasional 'I' and 'J' above it. ST BARNABAS is in large caps at the top.
> c.36 × 18; September 1902.

8 Inscription for choir seats, St Paul's, Carlton-in-the-Willows, Nottingham.

> This possibly refers to an inscription for the former pulpit, now destroyed; 'Sir, we would
> see Jesus' – virtually an encouragement to the preacher. January 1903.

8A/P Stone lintel above the door of Christ Church, Brixton. Designed by Edward
Johnston. Architect, Beresford Pite.

> Large caps c.8 in. for 'Christ Church' and c.4 in. for 'Anno domini MDCCCCI'. The title is
> rather condensed, but with generous 'C's and a flat-based 'U', – the spacing therefore
> rather innocent. It is essentially integrated as part of the architecture, not appearing as an
> extra. (The foundation stone within the church, dated 1898, would seem to be by a
> different hand.)
> c.6 ft × 1 ft 6 in.; November 1903. (See also 43A/P)

9 The eighth Commandment: THOU SHALT NOT STEAL, at Madresfield Court,
near Malvern.

> The letters (3¼ in. high), surmounted by a cross, incised and gilded, are on a board 44 × 9
> wide, of stained oak screwed on to the panelling by the door of the library. Verticals are
> slightly widened towards the top – an interesting early quirk of originality. The 'E' and 'L'
> are wide, and the inclusion of serifs is somewhat arbitrary. The work was commissioned

by Graily Hewitt (a member of the Art Workers Guild) on behalf of the 7th Earl
Beauchamp (1872–1938). The words – only the NOT is undivided – are set in such wide
spaces that the minatory text, though sited to be seen by guests leaving the library,
resembles the panelling so closely as to be self-effacing. 1903.

10 Tablet on the outside wall, south of the main door, Holy Trinity, Sloane Street,
London in memory of Admiral Sir GEORGE OMMANEY WILLES, G.C.B., 1823–
1901 – 'the Gates and Railings of this Church were erected by his Widow'.
Architects, Sedding and Wilson.

> One of the earliest examples of Gill's use of strongly contrasted sizes of caps and lower
> case within a moulded frame carved in the general wall surface, thus setting back the face
> of the panel. The inscription is, typically, crowded to fill the frame – what E.G. called
> 'massed'.
> 19 × 20; 1903. (See also 266)

11 Inscription on the pediment of the former Medical School, Downing Street,
Cambridge: HUMPHREY MUSEUM in raised and 'V'-cut caps. Architect, E.S.Prior.

> Virtually on a continuation of the cornice.
> c.42 × 1; July 1903.

11A/P Inscription below the sill of an oriel window of the former Medical School,
Downing Street, Cambridge: DANS LES CHAMPS DE L'OBSERVATION LE
HASARD NE FAVORISE QUE LES ESPRITS PREPARES.

> This commission and No. 11 prompted the architect, Professor E.S.Prior, to suggest that
> Gill take up lettering full time. Resigning from the office of W.D.Caröe, he did so. The
> inscription is characterized by being very closely spaced, unexpected tall strokes for 'P',
> 'L', 'T' and 'F' and a clear integration with the architecture – virtually a band of texture.
> c.11 ft long; July 1903.
>
> (The Inventory records an additional inscription, diamond shaped, MEDICAL SCHOOL,
> cut in November 1915, but there is no sign of this now.)

12 A series of twenty-eight copper repoussé panels in the hall of Charterhouse
School, Godalming, recording the names of scholars; panels of standard sizes,
about 10 in. square. Architect, W.D.Caröe.

> There is frequent use of joined caps for long names to reduce them to the standard
> width. A note on the drawing explains, letters 'beaten up from the back', and 'W.D.C. is
> responsible.' 1903.

13 Epitaph incised direct on the southeast face of the chancel arch in St Mary's,
Burpham, Arundel, Sussex: BLESSED ARE THE PEACEMAKERS, in memory of
FRANCIS JOHN MOUNT, Archdeacon of Chichester, 1831–1903. (See Plate II in
the Inventory.)

> There is a cheerful informality in the use of large caps asymmetrically placed.
> c.12 × 12; August 1903.

14 Headstone for grave in Harrow Cemetery, London, in memory of EMILY
ADELAIDE MAKINS, d.1903.

> An early occasion of the introduction of mixed letter-forms – roman caps, lower case,

AD MAIOREM DEI GLORIAM

THIS·STONE·WAS·LAID
BY
THE·RIGHT·HONOVRABLE·FRANK·GREEN
LORD·MAYOR·OF·LONDON
ON·SATVRDAY·OCTOBER·5th·1901
THIS·CHVRCH·IS·ERECTED·OVT·OF·THE·FVNDS
ARISING·FROM·THE·SALE·OF
S·MICHAEL·BASSISHAW·E·C
E·A·B·SANDERS·VICAR·OF·EDMONTON

3 Massed text and 'nesting' letters, St Michael's, Edmonton, 1901 (4).

LES·CHAMPS·DE·L'OBSERVATION

4 Part of an 11-ft long inscription below the sill of the former Medical School, Cambridge, 1903 (11A/P).

5 A familiar shop fascia in use from 1903 to 1975, 1903 (16).

+

THOU SHALT NOT STEAL

6   A warning in the library at Madresfield Court, Worcester, 1903 (9).

L·N·GUILLEMARD·c
F·LONGWORTH·DAMES·c
W·F·SHEPPARD   M
E·St·A·WAKE   S
G·L·DICKINSON

7   One of 28 copper repoussé panels, with joined or small letters to help the spacing, 1903 (12).

rRRR
RRRR

8   Early development of Eric Gill's capital 'R', 1900–1914.

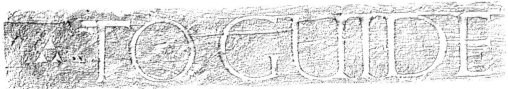

A TO GUIDE

9   Detail of rubbing of 4 in. letters on oak, Great Warley, Essex, 1903 (17).

italic and numerals. On the drawing is the estimate – £1 for small letters, £1 for capitals, 10s for expenses, total £2 10s 0d.

R 22 × 17; August 1903.

15 War memorial in Danejohn Park, Canterbury, for the 1st and 2nd Volunteer Battalions 'THE BUFFS' and ROYAL EAST KENT IMPERIAL YEOMANRY.

There are three large full-size drawings. This fine inscription (still with a capital 'U' with a flat base) is now covered by a poorly lettered bronze tablet. The tall obelisk with boldly classical base may readily be attributed to Caröe. September 1903. (See also 32)

16 Painted letters on fascia and in the tea-room of bookshop for W.H.Smith & Son, rue de Rivoli, Paris.

Several similar jobs were done for W.H.Smith which led to the adoption of the same style of lettering for their bookshops and railway bookstalls throughout Great Britain, and in use till about 1975. The fine details for the letters survive in the company's archives. The 'W', 'H' and 'S' are separated by central square dots, derived from Johnston. A good early example, 15 ft wide, is in Baker Street Underground station.

Lettering (for fascia): 30 × 22; September 1903. (See also 29)

(In Architectural Heritage Year, 1975, the W.H.Smith shopfront in Newtown, Powys, was restored as a complete example of E.G.'s contribution, not only the roman caps at about 6 in. and 3 in. but also the advertisement panels in glazed tiles: 'Guide books and maps of all parts', 'Newspapers regularly delivered', 'Diestamping and engraving' etc.)

17 Three incised inscriptions on a panel and two oak beams, 10 ft long, on lych gate of St Mary's, Great Warley, Essex.

A   THIS LYCH GATE WAS ERECTED ANNO DOMINI MCMIII IN THE REIGN OF KING EDWARD VII.

B   TO GUIDE OUR FEET INTO THE WAY OF PEACE.

C   I WILL STRENGTHEN THEE, YEA I WILL HELP THEE.

Architect, Harrison Townsend.

On the panel the 2½ in. caps have a 'T' and an 'I' arbitrarily taken up as at Downing St, Cambridge (11A). The grand inscriptions along the beams are an early example of aptness of choice for their position. On entering the churchyard for a funeral – a lych gate is after all a 'corpse-gate' – the mourners read 'to guide our feet into the way of peace': and on leaving it after the burial, 'I will strengthen thee, yea I will help thee'. There is the flat-based 'U', generous 'C', 'D' and 'G', and Johnston's criss-crossed 'W'; and somewhat naive spacing (as in 11A). In panel (A) Johnston's space-fillers of lines and square dots are used. October 1903.

18 Brass plate for Langport School, Somerset, recording the gift of a bench and tools, by J.T.Knight, C.C., in the name of his two sons ASHTON & ARCHIBALD KNIGHT, O.L.'s, September 1903.

This is the first of E.G.'s metal plates.

8 × 20; October 1903.

19 Copper repoussé panel in St David's Church, Exeter. A four-line inscription recording the gift of the south transept window in memory of RICHARD BOWERMAN WEST D.L, d.1900.

Apart from the name in caps, the panel is in well-spaced, but still naive lower-case roman – straight vertical descenders for 'f' and 'y', and arbitrary ascenders for 'd'; unusually the lines are centred. The secret fixings to the wall ensure as much architectural integration as possible. Was lettering in relief chosen to respond to the side light from the window?
c. 30 × 9; October 1903.

(On the south wall of the nave of St David's, Exeter is the memorial of Arthur Hoskyn, Officer of Inland Revenue, Sergeant in the 27th (Devon) Yeomanry, killed in action at Vlakfontein, S. Africa, 1901 aged 23. It relates to a window above, dedicated by his brother officials of the Inland Revenue. The tablet is in Lombardic lettering in copper repoussé (10 × 39) and is probably the origin of E.G.'s use of this method.)

20 Tombstone in Nunhead Cemetery, Kent, in memory of ANNIE GILL, 1858–1879, and of her father The Revd GEORGE GILL, 1820–1880, for sixteen years a missionary in the South Sea Islands and nineteen years Minister of the Westgate Congregational Chapel, Burnley. Also of SARAH, his wife, 1818–1898. (George and Sarah Gill were E.G.'s grandparents.) (See Plate III in the *Inventory*.)

Two early layouts survive, one with a panel of massed roman caps, which was super-seded in favour of the emphasis on the daughter Annie as opposed to her parents. At the top the lower case 'f' is extended for 1 ft with a flourish.
R 58 × 30; November 1903.

20A Alphabet designed for cutting in stone. An outline drawing of 2½ in. letters; signed A. E. R. Gill.

A note reads: 'Dedicated to EFM. Being the best I can do at this time, therefore dedicated as above.' ('EFM' refers to Ethel Foster Moore, his future wife.) November 1903.

21 Lettering for inscription on metal: HE THAT BELIEVETH IN CHRIST SHALL HAVE ETERNAL LIFE.

A drawing of widely spaced roman caps, verticals slightly widened at the tops (cf 9).
11 × 13; c. 1903.

22 Inscription on Hopton-Wood stone: GLORIA IN ALTISSIMIS DEO.

A description together with a collotype reproduction (Plate XXIV) is in Edward Johnston's *Writing & Illuminating & Lettering*, pp. 486–7. Intended to go over a lintel; E.G. explained that the 5 in. caps – DEO – well spaced out, are of the same apparent weight as the smaller 2 in. lines. The 'I' and 'L' are taller.
R 17 × 29; 1903.

23 Inscription in Latin in memory of ARTHUR HAROLD WEBSTER, d. 1902, in the South African cloister at Charterhouse.

The drawing bears a pencilled note: 'This was done under compulsion. A.E.R.G.' – probably referring to a requirement by Caröe to use Lombardic, the favourite letter form in use in his office.

The classical wall memorial in alabaster is readily attributable to Caröe, with a fine coat of arms above and a shield below. Webster's association, like Caröe's, was with Charterhouse and Trinity College, Cambridge.
c. 40 × 22; c. 1903.

24 Inscription in memory of MARY CONSTANCE SMITH, Deaconess, d. 1902.

16 × 9; c. 1903.

This window was inserted by many parishioners & friends
In memory of RICHARD·BOWERMAN-WEST·D·L
& as an expression of gratitude for his generous gifts
to the building of this Church
He died 8th August 1900

10   Rubbing of a copper repoussé tablet, with secret fixings to the wall, St David's, Exeter, 1903 (19).

TO THE GLORY OF GOD
AND THE EXTENSION
OF HIS KINGDOM
THIS MEMORIAL STONE OF THE
CHURCH OF S·BARTHOLOMEW
STAMFORD HILL·WAS LAID BY
SIBELL·COUNTESS GROSVENOR
ON ASCENSION DAY 1903

11   Boldly raised caps, with occasional joined letters, St Bartholomew, Stamford Hill, London N.16, 1903 (27).

ARTVRO   FVND   RNH

AND   James   JAMES

MRS   J   BROWNE

12   Joined letters: 1. Arthur Webster memorial, Charterhouse, 1903 (23); 2. St Michael's, Edmonton, 1901 (4); 3. Royal Northern Hospital, Islington, 1923 (431); 4. St Bartholomew's, Stamford Hill, 1903 (27); 5. John Kipling's grave, Knebworth, 1907 (119); 6. Fletcher memorial, Ilkley, 1904 (40); 7. Cobbe memorial, Manchester College, Oxford, 1908 (153).

25 Lettering: ANNO CORONATIONIS ED. VII REG.

> Another version reads 'ANNO ED. VII REG. CORONATI' with the date. This appears to have been on a building in Knightsbridge, now demolished. c.1903.

*26 A sort of raised ledgerstone shaped to form a cross in relief with a flat square centre and relief inscriptions, in the churchyard of Holy Trinity, Bradpole, Dorset, in memory of WILLIAM HOUNSELL of Wykes Court, 1820–1903.

> Arguably the most unusual layout of lettering on any of E.G.'s memorials. The name is divided by the arms of the cross; the rest of the words are within four rhomboidal panels vigorously divided by the wide arms of the cross:

My covenant was with him	To him for the fear wherewith he fear
of life and peace and I gave them	-ed me & was afraid before my name Mal 2.5

> (Malachi 2.6 would have been more appropriate, if true.) All in raised caps with a large initial 'M'. Below all this the sides of the stone are generously bevelled.
> 72 × 28; c.1903.

27 Foundation stone, St Bartholomew, Stamford Hill, London, N.16, Ascension Day, May, 1903. Architect, W.D.Caröe.

> This is in splendidly bold roman caps carved in relief, with some joined letters and a cross of sorts at the corner; the back is also carved.
> 18 × 36; 1903.

28 Inscription for memorial to CICILIA ROBINSON, Deaconess, d.1903, aged 33.

> 17 × 9; 1903.

29 Tablet: THE HOME LIBRARY for W.H.Smith & Son, London.

> The drawing 3 × 21, signed: 'for W.H.Smith & Son, per Mr Hornby. Jan 22, 1903. A.E.R.G.' This appears to be the first job done for W.H.Smith & Son, predating the fascia on their shops in Paris (16). 1903.

30 Panel of 4 in. letters, cut in oak: STUDY QUIET.

> Signed A.E.R.Gill, for Edward Johnston.
> R 5 × 43; 1904.

31 Painted letters on name board for the INNS OF COURT RIFLE VOLUNTEERS. This appears to have been in the Holborn area.

> March 1904.

32 Inscription recording the gift by the Mayor and Corporation of Canterbury of the site for the War Memorial to 'THE BUFFS' and ROYAL EAST KENT IMPERIAL YEOMANRY in Danejohn Park, Canterbury.

> This is within a classical moulding on the curved base of the memorial, doubtless carved in situ.
> 12 × 65; 1904. (See also 15)

33 Foundation stone for the Whitefield Memorial Chapel, Tottenham Court Road, London, W.1, April 1904. (Destroyed in the bombing, 1940.)

34 Lettering for W.H.Smith and Son: FOR ADVERTISING SPACES on this Railway apply to W. H. SMITH & SON 186 Strand, London W.C. Also: BOOKBINDING OF EVERY DESCRIPTION.

Indexed in the *Inventory* as in Westminster. 1904.

35 Fascia for W.H.Smith & Son's bookshop at Clacton-on-Sea, Essex.

June 1904.

36 Memorial tablet to HENRY W. RENDELL, 1866–1903.

Caps in four lines.
10 × 13; June 1904.

37 Foundation stone for the Working Men's College, Royal College St, Camden Town, London. LAID BY H.R.H. THE PRINCE OF WALES July 1904. Architect, W.D.Caröe.

Fine texture of bold raised caps, centred, with quirks of character such as an arbitrary tall 'T', and the splitting of 'com-mittee' … The wording is unusual – 'this first stone of the new home … In memory of Frederick Denison Maurice and of those who worked with him and followed in his footsteps.'
R 24 × 39; June 1904.

38 Memorial dedicated to the memory of WILLIAM PATON of the Royal Artillery, to commemorate his gallantry in action with C Battery, E Brigade, R.H.A., at the battle of Maiwand, 1880, d.1904. Also in memory of his wife AGNES, 1904.

An exceptional piece of lettering at Woolwich, destroyed in wartime bombing, c.1940.
R 38 × 28; July 1904.

38A/P Gilt frame for a mirror, a wedding present from E.G. to Ethel Mary Moore. In raised caps: MY LOVE IS LIKE A RED RED ROSE THAT'S NEWLY SPRUNG IN JUNE / MY LOVE IS LIKE A MELODY THAT'S SWEETLY PLAYED IN TUNE. Now in the possession of the Keatley Trust.

The chunky letters virtually form the top and bottom parts of the frame. The decoration was designed by Mary Gill, who had a studio in the loft of their new home at 20 Black Lion Lane, Hammersmith. August 1904.

39 Fascia for W.H.Smith & Son's bookshop at Bournemouth.

August 1904.

*40 Cross in Ilkley Cemetery, Yorks., in memory of ELIZABETH CATHERINE FLETCHER, d.10 January 1904.

One of E.G.'s greatest early works for the controlled freedom and originality of treatment. The lettering is raised from the surface of the tall sandstone cross, with a simple moulding on the edge, giving a unity of design and material. The overall texture of the inscription in which words fill the lines comes from much joining of letters and the use of occasional much smaller letters. 1904.

*41 Inscription WESTCOTT HOUSE over the arched doorway of this theological college in Jesus Lane, Cambridge.

13 *Sandstone cross, Ilkley, showing affinity of lettering and material, 1904 (40).*

The raised letters are generously wide and the upper word sits immediately above the lower: this gives the by now familiar solidly architectural unity of text and wall-surface. It seems to be the first job on which he cut – at the lower right-hand corner – a Latin cross with four dots, which was a kind of signature.

(An earlier scheme was for CLERGY TRAINING SCHOOL, in 4 in. caps, in relief and WESTCOTT HOUSE in two lines of 6 in. caps, accompanied by a mitre. The sketch is signed Gill & Hewitt.)

R 12 × 45; September 1904.

42 Tombstone with a bronze plate in memory of EMMA SOPHIA GALTON.

18 × 7; September 1904.

43 Inscription proposed in memory of Dean FREDERICK WILLIAM FARRAR, 1830–1903.

For Canterbury Cathedral, to be done in September 1904. But the memorial in the nave cannot be attributed to E.G.

*43A/P Painted inscriptions at Christ Church, Brixton, London, S.W.9 to a scheme by Edward Johnston on the eastern arch and the pendentives of the dome – Ten Commandments, the Summary of the Law, the Lord's Prayer and the Creed. Architect, Beresford Pite.

Architectural integration, assurance and asymmetry. Three sizes of caps, red and black. There is a vigorous asymmetry in the siting of the large caps with a series of five 'T's close to the right-hand side of the arch and T.T.A.O below related to the verse numbers from St Matthew 22 in red. GOD is large and centred at the top: AMEN is small, set vertically at the foot of each pendentive. (In a letter to Johnston of 14 November 1902, Pite covers the inclusion of 'your fee with the other items as setting out the text on the apse wall and drafting the name label over the door, so as to make all the use of you that I can for what fee you think proper.' In June 1903 a cheque was sent for £21, 'to include E.G.'s expenses.' Was this all?!)

The whole scheme, inspired by Johnston, is one of E.G.'s grandest in scale, and skill in layout. c.1904. (See also 8A/P)

44 Granite ledgerstone in the cloister of Canterbury Cathedral in memory of Archbishop FREDERICK TEMPLE – 1821–1902.

This is carved in relief with a great maltese cross and the Canterbury shield, the pallium of which forms part of the design of the cross. The lettering is typical Lombardic, no doubt to Caröe's requirement. October 1904.

(At the foot a later, leaded inscription by another hand records Beatrice Blanche Temple, 1844–1915.)

44A/P Bronze tablet with lettering in relief on memorial of Archbishop Frederick Temple in the Corona Chapel at Canterbury.

These are typical joined letters to get the spacing right. 'He lived through the reigns of William IV & Victoria, and crowned Edward VII.' Architect, W.D.Caröe; sculptor, F.W.Pomeroy.

12 × 30; c.1905.

45 Headstone in memory of PERCY ROBERT BASIL FEILDING second son of the Seventh Earl of Denbigh, 1827–1904, at St Peter's, Monks Kirby, Warwickshire.

Exceptional early caps and numerals: massed.
R 24 × 22; October 1904.

45A/P Tall cross adjoining 45 – MAKE THEM TO BE NUMBERED WITH THY
SAINTS: CHRIST SAID HE THAT BELIEVETH IN ME HATH EVERLASTING LIFE.

Interesting massed caps on base of cross; JESUS in raised letters at the top. c.1904.

*46 The Ten Commandments, in Holy Trinity Church, Charwelton, nr Rugby, in
black red and other colours on two panels beside the high altar. Above the panels
lettered in black and red: GOD SPAKE THESE WORDS AND SAID, I AM THE
LORD THY GOD: THOU SHALT HAVE NO OTHER GODS BUT ME.

Then follow the rest, numbered in roman numerals on the frame of the panelling, and
signed A.E.R.G. between the arms of a cross. Pen-drawn direct on to oak panels, with
brightly painted initials. The final words of certain commandments are flourished out for
some distance to fill the space: the final 'r' of 'murder' runs out curve after curve for 14 in.
to finish in a snake's head. The 'y' of 'adultery' extends in three branches for 2 ft 4 in. and
is decorated with twenty-one coloured flowers rather larger than those elsewhere.
26 × 26 each; November 1904.

47 Foundation stone laid by Mrs W.H.Brown, 12 May 1904. The inscription reads:
THIS STONE WAS / LAID ON MAY XII / MCMIV / BY MRS. H. BROWN / He
shall make thee a joy / of many generations …

R 26 × 26; 1904.

48 Oak panel, with a shield over, for the Hospital for Sick Children, Great Ormond
Street, London, in memory of Nurse ELEANOR FIELD, for fifteen years at the
Hospital and for thirteen years at the Nurses' Hostel, d.1903.

17 × 25; c.1904.

49 Memorial stone laid by JOHN HENNELL, B.A., 9 July, 1904. Signed 'A.E.R.G.'
R 18 × 34; c.1904.

50 Tablet of incised letters: G.E.O., LL.D. VICARIUS MCMIV.
R 9 × 13; c.1904.

51 Tablet at Laurence Sheriff School, Rugby, in memory of HENRY VICTOR
WHITEHOUSE, 1889–1904.

A sophisticated layout and a finely worded inscription; not, as stated in the Inventory, 1904.
c.1937. (See 680A/P)

52 Foundation stone for a Mission Hall of the GOOD SHEPHERD and TEMPLE
INSTITUTE in Garrett's Lane, Wandsworth, laid by Beatrice Blanche Temple,
widow of the Archbishop of Canterbury; 'as approved by W.G.O.'.

Fine roman caps in seven lines, with taller 'T's and 'I's and some fun with the 'S'. Now
demolished.
R 17 × 26; 1905.

53 Carvings at St John the Divine, Richmond, Surrey. Architect, Arthur Grove
(d.1929) sometime partner of E.S.Prior.

14   Boldly massed caps, Jesus Lane, Cambridge, 1904 (41).

15   Detail from the Ten Commandments, pen-drawn on oak; the final 'y' of 'adultery', Charwelton Church, 1904 (46).

A 'SACRISTY' in relief, below an elaborate cross within a roundel.

An original treatment of bold roman letters in relief within a dentilled border.

B Lettering below the Calvary, on the gable of the church: GOD SO LOVED THE WORLD –

Four dots as a space filler beside THE, and small letters to get the space filled appropriately. February 1905. (See also 54, 131, 213, 262)

54 Numerals for hymn boards for St John the Divine, Richmond, Surrey.

The hymn boards are surmounted by a roundel in relief and gilt, containing 'S' and 'J' beside a chalice containing a serpent, a traditional symbol for St John. February 1905.

55 Fascia for W.H.Smith & Son's bookshop at Leicester.

March 1905.

56 Fascia for W.H.Smith & Son's bookshop at Southport.

March 1905.

57 Inscription in Latin on stone tablet in the ante-chapel of Brasenose College, Oxford, in memory of ALBERT WATSON: ET BENEFACTORE EXIMIUS. d. November 1904.

This appears to be E.G.'s first use of pilasters (here with 'A W' forming the capitals) and an architectural frame for the lettering. There is a nice contrast between the large roman caps and the lines of lower case. The capital 'M's have an innocent informality. March 1905.

58 Incised tablet in memory of HENRY CROMPTON, 1836–1904.

The full-size drawing refers to dates 48 and 50/116 as being 'of the "Positivist Calendar".' 7 × 15; April 1905.

59 Painted notice board for St John's, Bognor Regis.

April 1905.

60 Inscription on paving round a pool at Newnham College, Cambridge, in memory of HENRY SIDGWICK, 1905.

With a 12 in. 'H' and 'S', and 6 in. caps for the rest, this has been re-cut by another hand, evidently without referring to the original drawing, which has a large detail of the 'S'. E.G.'s note on the drawing says 'Lecture: N.B. only use one tool if possible'.

The wording of the memorial deserves quoting, probably phrased by E.G. to allow for encircling the flat paving round the pool, 'The daughters of this house to those that shall come after commend the filial remembrance of Henry Sidgwick 1905.' April 1905. (See also 290)

61 Painted letters on fascia and signboards for W.H.Smith & Son's shop at Moseley, Birmingham.

This version has a tall 'T', and a note in E.G.'s hand 'N.B. Don't do this if you can help it.' May 1905.

62 Fascia for W.H.Smith & Son's bookshop at Scarborough.

May 1905.

*63 Inscription for the University College of South Wales and Monmouth, Cardiff.

This long high-relief inscription in Latin is carved on the abutment of the central arch at the University of Wales in the Civic Centre in Cardiff. In thirteen lines of roman caps it is a remarkably restrained work, very much part of the design of the building, rather than just the usual foundation stone. The roman caps are fairly free in style, with very little contraction for space-filling's sake. Caröe's name as architect is for once spelt correctly with a diagonal stroke through the 'O'.

c. 3 ft square; May 1905.

64 Tombstone of BLANCHE MARY SHORE CLOUGH 1828–1904 at Burley, Hants.

An exceptional early stone comprising, on a superimposed tablet, six lines of massed, raised lettering, followed by date of death and a (Johnstonian) flower. The 'C' of Clough forms a large central feature.

c. 18 × 18; May 1905.

65 Inscription recording the gift by Thomas Henry Lyon of the plans of a church (in Melbourne, Australia?) in memory of his sister CAROLINE LOUISA LYON.

T. H. Lyon was an architect in Cambridge.

R 16 × 16; May 1905.

66 Brass tablet in St Wilfred's Church, Bognor Regis, in memory of JAMES ALLEN FREEBORN HOWELL, 1887–1904.

This tablet was the joint work of Eric Gill, and his brother Macdonald. The lettering (mainly italic) is filled with red wax for the name, the rest in black.

Illustrated in Lawrence Weaver's *Memorials and Monuments*, 1915.

R 17 × 16; May 1905.

67 Stone tablet at St Bartholomew, Brightwell Baldwin, Oxon., in memory of RICHARD DU CANE, d. January 1904.

A small and distinguished tablet with no surrounding moulding within the rough stone walling of the porch. The top line is filled out with crosses to the edge of the stone: four lines centred, the last two ranged to the left, the caps and certain numerals very large: cheerful flourishes at the sides.

R 9 × 15; July 1905. (See also 88)

68 Stone base of an elaborate oak cross at Clovelly, Devon, in memory of MARY CHRISTINE MANNERS, daughter of John, Lord Manners & of Constance his wife. Died at Bangalore, India, 15 February 1904, aged 17 years.

The inscription responds to the curved shape of the stone forming the socket for the cross – 'For a few short years the light of many lives she sleeps beside the home which had been appointed her for possession but that God first called her to a greater inheritance.'

R 19 × 27; August 1905. (See also 97)

69 Tombstone, at Kingussie, Highland Region, in memory of LUCY McEWEN HASLAM, 1857–1904.

Among various freedoms such as two sorts of 'W', the leg of a capital 'K' extends for over 12 in.

R 14 × 27; September 1905.

70 Tablet (in a cathedral in Australia?) beneath a stone seat from Rochester Cathedral built by Bishop Gundulf, d.1108. The inscription reads: THE CATHEDRAL CHURCH / OF CHRIST & OUR LADY OF / ROCHESTER SENDS GREET'G / WITH THE ABOVE STONE FROM / BP. GUNDULF'S CATHEDRAL: / A.D. 1074.

> Caps and lower case, with certain unexpected freedoms such as the top of an 'f' taken to the left.
> R 9 × 12; September 1905.

71 Signboard at Stoke-on-Trent for JOSIAH WEDGWOOD Ltd.

> October 1905.

72 Three Brass nameplates for 29B Lincoln's Inn Fields, London, W.C.2, for ALFRED H. POWELL, e.g. RING AND ENTER.

> E.G. also designed a nameplate for this architect's house in Red Lion Square, 1906.
> R 5 × 12, 2 × 6, and 5 × 11; December 1905.

73 Relief inscription on Hopton-Wood stone: PAX HUIC DOMUI.

> R 9 × 9; c.1905.

74 Relief inscription with a decorative border on Hopton-Wood stone: SUSSEX HOUSE; for Emery Walker's workshop in Hampshire Hog Lane, Hammersmith, London, W.6.

> R 10 × 15; 1905.

75 Brass plate for a window in memory of EDWARD PREST of York, his wife and eldest daughter, also of JAMES WILLIAMSON, d.1899, and of C.G. WALE, second daughter of E. Prest, d.1905.

> Fine upper and lower case and space filling: with a ½ in. wide decorative border.
> R 9 × 18; c.1905.

*75A/P Wall tablet to Lt. Col. Charles WYNNE-FINCH in Pentrefoelas Church, near Betws-y-Coed, Gwynedd, d.1905.

> Perfect integration (cf 122) of inscription with the shape of Caröe's tablet: nine lines, caps, lower case and the usual italic for 'A faithful friend is a strong defence and he that hath found such an one hath found a treasure.' Four jolly flourishes. c.1905. (See 122)

76 Letters 'I O' incised on stone.

> Letters 2 in. high beneath which is a cross. Also inscribed: 'I.A.E.R.G. 9. 05.'
> R 6 × 4; September 1905.

77 Tablet of Hopton-Wood stone with incised inscription: IN PRINCIPIO / ERAT VERBUM ET / VERBUM ERAT APUD / DEUM ET DEUS ERAT VERBUM; cut for exhibition purposes.

> R 8 × 13; 1905.

77A Hopton-Wood stone tablet inscribed: DAS WIR UNS IN IHR ZERSTREUEN DARUM IST DIE WELT SO GROSS: cut presumably for Count Kessler.

> c.1905.

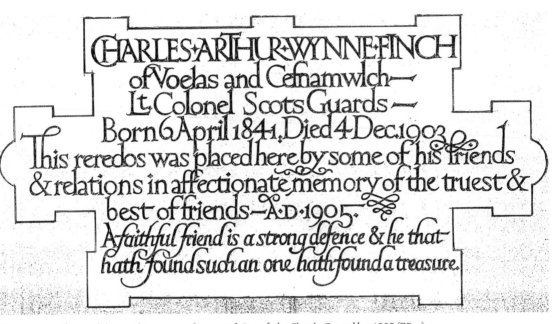

CHARLES·ARTHUR·WYNNE·FINCH
of Voelas and Cefnamwlch—
Lt·Colonel Scots Guards—
Born 6 April 1841, Died 4 Dec.1903
This reredos was placed here by some of his friends
& relations in affectionate memory of the truest &
best of friends—A·D·1905.
A faithful friend is a strong defence & he that
hath found such an one hath found a treasure.

6   Integration of text and shape within a strapwork memorial, Pentrefoelas Church, Gwynedd, c.1905 (75A/P).

17   High-relief massed caps for a foundation stone within an arcade, University of Wales, Cardiff, 1905 (63).

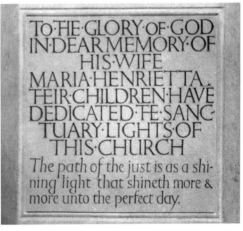

TO·THE·GLORY·OF·GOD
IN·DEAR·MEMORY·OF
HIS·WIFE
MARIA·HENRIETTA.
FEIR·CHILDREN·HAVE
DEDICATED·FE·SANC
TUARY·LIGHTS·OF
THIS·CHURCH
The path of the just is as a shi-
ning light that shineth more &
more unto the perfect day.

18   Detail of a pier, cut in situ at Upton-on-Severn Church, c.1906 (87A).

78 Inscription on Hopton-Wood stone: 'A' and 'V' interlaced, followed by an Omega surrounding a 'T', are simply placed above 'non est'.

> It has been suggested that it may be some cabalistic or alchemical rebus.
> R 10 × 15; 1905.

79 Camber-arched headstone with relief inscription on York stone at St John's, Burley, Hants in memory of LILY FRANCES KATHERINE, wife of John Colquhoun Duff, d. 1905.

> The inscribed part is set within a deep frame; the lines widely spaced, the letters raised from the surface, and slightly dished in section. A simple and very distinguished stone.
> 49 × 27; c. 1906.

80 Oak tablet commemorating the gift of cross and candlesticks in memory of 'HENRY CHARLES RICHARDS, K.C., M.P. for this Borough' (i.e. East Finchley), 1895–1905, d. 1905.

> Below the reredos in the Lady Chapel, St Andrew, Holborn. Four lines, 'F' 'S' 'R' 'K' and an ampersand all nicely extended. Now gilded.
> R 6 × 24; c. 1906.

81 Inscription in memory of CANON FREDERICK GEORGE HUME SMITH, Rector of St Bartholomew's, Armley, Leeds, d. 1905. 'In quietness and confidence shall be your strength.'

> The final letter is flourished out for some distance.
> R 11 × 12; c. 1906.

82 Gravestone of Portland stone, surmounted by a Celtic cross with relief inscription in memory of CAROLINE FRANCIS – 1824–1905, at St James's, Burlingham, Worcestershire. On the back is 'C.F. d. 27 July 1905'.

> An unusual small cross with interlacing pattern like a tree and bold raised letters.
> R 36 × 24; c. 1906.

83 Inscriptions for gateway of the W. H. SMITH MEMORIAL HALL and a sunk panel: ERECTED AS A WORKMEN'S CLUB IN MEMORY OF W. H. SMITH, M.P. Another inscription: THIS HALL IS ERECTED IN MEMORY OF THE RIGHT HONOURABLE W. H. SMITH, M.P.

> An exceptional layout, stated in the Inventory index as in Westminster, but the site is still undiscovered.
> R 18 × 49; c. 1906.

84 Inscription on stone: ST DYFRIG'S CLERGY HOUSE, formerly in Fitzsimmon's Place, Cardiff, now demolished.

> E.G. drew a section to indicate the exact form of the raised letters. The 'celtic' treatment produced an odd capital 'G', but a good curly-tailed 'Y': an exceptional design.
> R 5 × 30; January 1906. (See also 118)

85 Sandstone cross in Torquay cemetery, 'Here lieth the body of THOMAS RIDGWAY BRIDSON' – 1823–1904.

> Only two bits of the shaft survive: but there remains enough to admire the originality of the 'V'-cut lettering on a narrow width, which rivals the raised letters on Mrs Fletcher's

cross-shaft at Ilkley (40). To fill the space letters are joined, shortened or overlapped. A full 'V'-cut cross at the top.

R 30 × 9; April 1906.

86 Tombstone inventoried in error as in St Marylebone Cemetery, London, N.2, in memory of HENRY PRINCE, Civil Engineer, 1831–1906. Location unknown.

Lettering in relief.
R 5 × 6; May 1906.

87 Gravestone in Brompton Cemetery, London, S.W.10, with a recessed circle at the top bearing an inscription in memory of EDWARD HUGHES, d.1876, and of his son WILLIAM ARTHUR HUGHES, d.1899.

Below the circle is carved – without appearing an afterthought – an inscription to Harriet Hughes, d.1908. The whole stone is distinguished by simple mouldings round the circle and extending below it.
15 in. diameter; May 1906.

*87A Inscription on a pier in the church at Upton-on-Severn, Worcs., in memory of GEORGE EDWARD MARTIN of Ham Court, 1829–1905 and commemorating a window given by his friends; below, a memorial to his widow MARIA HENRIETTA.

This grand work – nineteen lines of closely spaced caps and three lines of italics below – has great freedom in layout and letter form: some joined letters, some small, or taller, some words in rather wider letters to help fill the lines; some lines centred, some justified to the left; straight-legged 'R's, flat-based 'U's, generous 'G's and 'D's, fine numerals. The phrasing of the inscription and the way the words fit the lines may partly be attributable to E.G. – 'To his energy and / self denial the / building of this / House of God for the Parish of Upton / was mainly due.' At the base is a little flourished foot to an 'H'. The additional eight lines of caps (plus three of italics) is characteristic of E.G.'s work, the main text centred, the minor justified to the left, and with divided words and ampersands to suit the filling of the lines. The main text has five letters joined to get the texture right. A narrow moulding surrounds each inscription. The italic texts are from Psalm 26: 'Lord, I have loved the habitation of thy house.'
R 54 × 24; c.1906.

*88 Cross in memory of RICHARD DU CANE, d.1904, and of his wife CHARLOTTE MARIA, d.1902, in the churchyard at Horsmonden, Kent. Other names were added in 1907 and 1919.

The base of the cross is virtually formed of lettering, each section divided centrally by a strong moulding. Some of the names are very large, the details generally solidly massed, the numerals nicely varied to suit the spaces. Contractions include IN MEM, SHL, DAUR. An exceptional example of lettering and of its integration into an architectural scheme.

The first names may well be the last lettering cut by E.G. before H.J.Cribb joined him in June 1906.
May 1906, and later. (See also 67)

(E.G. suggested that grave memorials square on plan and 3 ft – 6 ft high were an advantage, but 'suitable only in the event of there being a good many names to be commemorated' – i.e. which could be cut on the sides as they were needed.)

89 Inscriptions in the Chapel of the Ascension, Hyde Park Place, London, W.2 commissioned by Frederic Shields (d.1911) whose elaborate scriptural decorations adorned this building. (The chapel was destroyed in an air raid during World War II.)

> June 1906.

90 Brass plate, THE NEW ENGLISH ART CLUB, New Bond Street, London, commissioned by William Rothenstein.

> 14 × 22; June 1906.

91 Nameplate: A. RANDALL WELLS, Architect.

> R 4 × 10; June 1906.

92 Foundation stone on the left of the entrance to the Y.M.C.A., Bond Street, Ealing, London, W.5, laid by the Duke of Argyll, 7 July, 1906.

> Grand, widely spaced 3 in. caps for Y.M.C.A.
> 14 × 26; June 1906. (See also 116)

93 Marble inscription in memory of BRYDGES ROBINSON BRANFILL, J.P., 1833–1905.

> This contains a long extended lower case 'e' and a much flourished 'y'. Site unknown, stated in the Inventory as at St Laurence, Upminster.
> R 12 × 12; 1906.

94 Tombstone, with cross, in memory of JUDGE JAMES CHARLES WHITEHORNE, d.1905.

> From the drawings this contains the first capital 'J' without a cockspur serif. Site unknown, but stated in the Inventory to be at Leamington. The cross is believed to be about 6 ft high; and the kerbs, as shown on the drawing, well integrated with the design.
> R 11 × 15; 1906.

95 Inscriptions of gilded letters in St Luke's Church, Old Street, London, now demolished.

> 1906.

*96 Monument in St Helen's Church, Escrick, Yorks., with coat of arms and inscription in memory of STEPHEN WILLOUGHBY LAWLEY, 1823–1905, third son of Paul Beilby, Lord Wenlock; Rector of Escrick, 1848–1868, and sometime Sub-dean of York. The inscription also records the building of this church and Rectory House.

> This is a majestic tablet with twenty lines of characteristic inscription, one of the best early works by E.G. – large initials, and freedom inspired by Johnston. The general overall texture of lower case is enlivened by the placing of words in caps, or condensed. The fine gilded shield has an especially well-composed motto ribbon. The name 'Wenlock' in the bottom right-hand corner ends with a flourished 'k' in which are embodied E.G.'s initials and the date; one of the few works signed by him.
> R 40 × 50; August 1906.

> (Note: The gravestone of S. W. Lawley in Escrick churchyard with raised lettering in recessed lines was attributed to E.G. by the late George Pace, but this seems arguable in the light of the letter form.)

In memory of
STEPHEN·WILLOUGHBY·LAWLEY
third son of Paul Beilby, Lord Wenlock, and of
Caroline his wife. Rector of Escrick 1848-1868,
and sometime Sub-dean of York.
BORN at Escrick 4.April.1823, he was educated at Rugby School,
& at Balliol College, Oxford, & entered Holy Orders in 1846.
After his resignation of this benefice he passed his life in scho-
larly retirement & in the constant exercise of kindness & charity.
His chief literary work was the editorship of the York Breviary for
the Surtees Society in 1882. He died at Exminster in Devon in
his 83rd year: 23 Oct.1905 & lies buried in Escrick Churchyard.
BUT chiefly should here be recorded that the building of this
church of S HELEN, as also of the present Rectory House,
was due to his munificence & personal care. The church was built
to the memory of his father from the designs of F.C.Penrose, con-
sulting architect to the chapter of S.Pauls Cathedral, & was consecrated
by Thomas Musgrave, Archbishop of York, 1 July, 1857.
This record was placed here by his nephew Beilby, 3rd. Lord Wenlock,
who, as a child, laid the first stone of this building in 1856.

19   Lettering as texture, with lively details, and signed A.E.R.G., at St Helen's, Escrick, Yorks., 1906 (96).

20   Detail of coat of arms, St Helen's, Escrick, Yorks., 1906 (96).

*97 Inscription (letters in red) surmounted by a coat of arms in colour, in All Saints, Thorney Hill, Bransgore, Christchurch, Hants, commissioned by John, Lord Manners and his wife in memory of their daughter MARY CHRISTINE MANNERS, who died at Bangalore in her eighteenth year, 1904.

> In lower case, as at Escrick (96), this big memorial of eighteen lines in caps includes many special E.G. characteristics – centring of the main wording, justified to the left for the minor, a big initial 'S', extended 'E's – one with a clear mistake honestly left – occasional taller or smaller letters, the spacing casual, and topped by a fine gilded and coloured shield and motto – supported by winged cherubs (quite unlike the bas-relief angels which in the 1930s held E.G.'s shields at Jesus College and St John's, Cambridge.) At the end is E.G.'s 'sign' of a cross with four dots. (This church by Detmar Blow also contains two other exceptional inscriptions by E.G. – 340A and 389.)
> 73 × 41; August 1906. (See Plate IV in the *Inventory*.) (See also 68)

98 Zinc memorial tablet, for St John the Baptist Hospital, Winchester, (site not now known) in memory of HENRY JOHN WICKHAM (1889–1898) and FREDERICK PEERS WICKHAM (1899–1904) chaplains of the hospital.

> The drawing, signed A.E.R.Gill, Bognor, stated 'designed for Ernest Gimson'.
> 7 × 14; September 1906.

99 Gravestone at St Mary Magdalene, North Ockendon, Upminster, Essex, in memory of CHAMPION RUSSELL, 1820–1887. Now destroyed.

> R 12 × 13; July 1906.

*100 Cross-shaped headstone at Old Godalming Cemetery, Farncombe, in memory of CAPT. THEODOSIUS STUART RUSSELL, 1836–1906, Chief Constable of the West Riding of Yorkshire, 1876–1905. An additional inscription: In memory of LOUISA CHARLOTTE EMILY his wife, 1847–1923.

> Well integrated with the cross shape, the inscription has large caps for the name (and the name added later) over a broad texture of lower case – with the sprightly features of a large 'C' on the left and a cross in the centre, the stem of which was at the second stage devised to link with the 'O' of Louisa. An outstanding work.
> R 25 × 35 and 32 × 18; 1906 and 1924.

101 Sign for W.H.Smith & Son at Fetter Lane, London, E.C.4, now demolished.

> 1906.

*102 Inscription on pedestal of statue in Portland Place, London, W.1, erected by members of the Regent Street Polytechnic in memory of QUINTIN HOGG, 1845–1903.

> The southern face has three subtle changes of size of caps within the eleven lines, including the name and dates on a projecting stone at the top. The main emphasis is on HOGG and FOUNDER: minor stress is on ERECTED, POLYTECHNIC and MEMORY. All is centred, yet with a lively silhouette; and the 'R' of FOUNDER has a proudly extended leg. The leg is still straight, and the 'U's are still flat at the base. Sculptor: George Frampton. (The drawing for the inscription: 14 × 10 is signed 'A.E.R.Gill, Calligrapher.') 1906.
>
> There are two later inscriptions – to Alice A.Hogg 1845–1918; and the war memorial 1914–1918.

103 Inscription on Hopton-Wood stone in memory of ELIZA, 1814–1906, widow of the Revd Chambre Corker Townshend of Derry, Rosscarbery, Co. Cork.

> Characteristically by now the lines of caps finish with italic at the foot, embellished in this case with a fine flourish to the 'g' of 'everlasting arms'. It also bears a shell within a lozenge, presumably her arms.
> R 25 × 25; June 1907.

104 Hopton-Wood stone tablet on the wall of a former 'shooting box' on the Hempstead Estate, Holt, Norfolk, in memory of SAMUEL FOWLE, 1830–1906, keeper on the estate for forty-five years: 'ever a faithful servant and a pleasant companion.'

> Commissioned and designed by Edward Johnston for his brother Andrew. The tablet is set flush with the wall, related in size to the brick dimensions. The composition of the inscription is exceptional.
> R 24 × 22; 1906.

105 Inscription in memory of Revd HENRY GEORGE WATKINS, of Parkstone, Dorset, d. March 1906.

> A fine work, fifteen lines of roman caps carved directly on a stone wall.
> R 32 × 16; c.1906.

106 Kerbs for the grave of ALICE ELIZABETH BUSK, 1848–1906, at Winkfield, Berks., with a simple cross lying on it, large caps, lead filled.

> On the end in smaller caps 'His servants shall serve him & they shall see his face'; on the side, the dates and the memorial inscription are carefully of the right number of words to fill the length of the grave. The usual cross and four dots appear as a 'signature'. c.1906.

107 Inscription in memory of HELOISE DE MAILLY REIGHLEY, d.1906, at Winkfield, Berks.

> Apparently carved direct on the church wall.
> R 17 × 11; c.1906.

108 Inscription in memory of FLORENCE EMMA STEVENS d.1906: 'Because I live ye shall live also.'

> R 11 × 29; c.1906.

109 Inscription in memory of E. H. TUFNELL, d.1906.

> This very fine inscription appears to be on the centre of a cross.
> R 3 × 7; c.1906.

*110 Stone tablet, inscription surmounted by coat of arms, at St John's, Stone, nr Aylesbury, in memory of General Sir HENRY AUGUSTUS SMYTH, K.C.M.G., 1826–1906, Colonel Commandant Royal Artillery and sometime Governor and Commander-in-Chief of Malta.

> This important work has a fine coloured coat of arms, freely designed within the constraints of heraldry, with two crests, and a spiny mantling; the motto and KCMG ribbon are superbly lettered. The fifteen-line inscription in caps, lower case and italic has great authority, using wide spacing of caps as a feature. The italic is calligraphic, with a 'g' pre-dating the Perpetua italic type fount. (See Plate V in the Inventory.)

OCT was corrected to SEPT – the 'O' is still just visible. (The inscription on the lower portion of the tablet is by another hand.)

57 × 27; 1907.

*111 Wooden tablet and side panels in All Saints', Thelwall, Warrington, erected to commemorate EDWARD THE ELDER King of the English, AD 901–925, who, in the year 923, 'built the fortress & town' of Thelwall. The tablet also commemorates his coronation and that of EDWARD VII in 1902.

> The central panel has the background painted as a *trompe-l'oeil* of vellum nailed at the corners, lettered mostly in black; the capital letters in red with flowered line fillers in red and green. This is fixed on a panel splendidly framed and pedimented, surmounted by a coronet. The blue side panels have lettering raised in gesso, and gilded. That on the left has at the foot: 'Fecit Halfer Bros., London W'; that on the right has: 'F. C. Eden, Architect', and E.G.'s cross with dots – the cross in this case with generous serifs, almost like a swastika. This must be one of the most elaborate works ever influenced by Johnston, free in expression in painted, pen drawn and gilded lettering.
>
> The good choice of words is a characteristic of E.G.'s work: 'Victorious over the Danes, he preserved the blessings of Christianity, and established supremacy over all Britain … crowned at Kingston-on-Thames … by Plegmund, Archbishop of Canterbury, *himself a Cheshire man* …' 'AD CMXXIII In this year after harvest King Edward went with his forces to THELWALL and commanded the town to be built and occupied and manned … Anglo Saxon Chronicle' and 'Let us now praise famous men …' The inscriptions, especially the central panel, are close-textured, crowded to the edge.
> Centre panel 23 × 19: sides 25 × 11; January–March 1907.
>
> (See also the triptych memorial to the Revd W. B. Garrett-Botfield in Shifnal Church, Shropshire – 150A/P.)

*112 Oval tablet of white marble set in an alabaster frame, St Mary's, Bridport, in memory of HARRIET TEMPLER, 1817–1905.

> In a massed text of nineteen lines the name HARRIET is off-centre, and many quirks of character give life to the whole. This may be the first time the 'R' has a curve to the leg. The lower case gives every sign of having been set out with a pen or a double pencil. The mistake of cutting 'Wykes', and not 'Wykes Court', is boldly corrected by adding 'Court' in tiny letters between the lines, without a caret. The spacing is steady with no concessions to the varying line widths except to reduce the size of letter at the ends of six lines – in accordance with Johnston's teaching: cf p. 259 in *Writing & Illuminating & Lettering*. The dark alabaster frame has early examples of E.G.'s leaves, familiar in his engravings. The epitaph words are well chosen, 'For over fourscore years her large discerning mind kept pace with her great & tender heart both quickened by the love of Christ. Those who knew her & many who knew her not were the better that she lived. In His good time God answered her prayer & took her quietly to Himself for Jesus Christ's sake. Amen.'
> c. 3 ft high; 1906.

113 EVER THE DISCOURAGED RESOLUTE STRUGGLING SOUL OF MAN EVER THE SOUL DISSATISFIED CURIOUS UNCONVINCED AT LAST STRUGGLING TO-DAY THE SAME BATTLING THE SAME … On the base of a statue by Frederick Lessore for a Royal Academy exhibition. Location unknown.

> 1907.

Lord Jesus

21 Detail of the Russell gravestone, Old Godalming Cemetery, 1906 (100).

22 Triptych (and one of the side panels) commemorating Edward the Elder and Edward VII, Thelwall Church, Cheshire, 1907 (111).

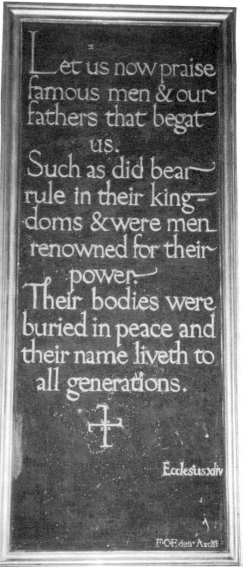

Let us now praise famous men & our fathers that begat us.
Such as did bear rule in their king-doms & were men renowned for their power.
Their bodies were buried in peace and their name liveth to all generations.

Ecclesus xliv

F·C·Eden· Arch⸗

114 Memorial tablet in Nunhead Cemetery, Kent, in memory of ANNIE PHELPS. Destroyed in the bombing of 1940.

> Mrs Phelps was the charwoman for Eric and Macdonald Gill at 16 Old Buildings, Lincoln's Inn. 1907.

115 Memorial plate for RICHARD COE.

> 1907.

116 Stone commemorating the opening of the Y.M.C.A., Bond Street, Ealing, London, w.5, by Lord Kinnaird (President, Y.M.C.A.), 17 April 1907, sited on the right of the entrance.

> The layout and letter forms do not seem to be by E.G.
> 14 × 26; 1907. (See also 92)

117 Signboard for Katharine Adams, bookbinder, for her bindery at Weston-sub-Edge, Broadway, Worcs., commissioned by Emery Walker.

> 1907.

117A/P Relief inscription in caps on an oak panel over the fireplace in the hall of Howgills Quaker Meeting House, Letchworth, Herts.: COME FORTH INTO THE LIGHT OF THINGS, W. WORDSWORTH.

> 43 × 11; c.1907.

117B/P A similar panel over the fireplace in the Meeting Room at Howgills, Letchworth. (By Gill and Christie for Miss Juliet Reckitt.) YOU MUST SIT DOWN SAYS LOVE AND TASTE MY MEAT, GEORGE HERBERT.

> 40 × 11; c.1907.

118 Stone commemorating the completion of St Dyfrig's Church, Wood Street, Cardiff, laid by Mrs Jenner on St Mark's Day, 1907.

> On the church's demolition Dr Cecil Gill, Eric's brother, rescued the stone, which was put in the entrance of the chapel at Capel-y-ffin. At the top 'SD' is incorporated into a double cross: on the big rectangular stone, big caps for S. DYFRIG'S CHURCH boldly divide the parts of the inscription treated like a texture.
> R 22 × 22; 1907.

*119 Portland headstone in memory of JOHN KIPLING – 1843–1906, head gardener at Knebworth House, Herts., commissioned by the Earl of Lytton.

> A stone freely shaped in the form of a cross to take the name in caps across the top, a long, crowded and affectionate tribute in the central panel, finishing with James 5.7–8 in italics and a generous interlaced flourish in the lower part. A fine unity of shape and text, as used by E.G. also at Farncombe, Surrey (100).
> R 36 × 22; 1907.

119A Stone tablet, letters incised: PUBLIC HOUSE TRUST, commissioned by the Earl of Lytton.

> 1907.

120 Foundation stone for the rectory at Finningham, Stowmarket, Suffolk, in memory of Revd TEMPLE FRERE, Rector of Finningham 1805–1829, laid by Winifred, daughter of John Tudor Frere.

> An almost unnoticeable stone on the corner of the house, yet with lettering, notably WINIFRED, well worth study: eleven lines of caps with the occasional 'T' taller; words divided as required by the space-filling texture.
> 24 × 23; 1907.

121 Inscription on Hopton-Wood stone forming a sarcophagus, placed below a window in the King Chapel, Ockham, near Leatherhead, to RALPH GORDON NOEL MILBANKE, D.L., 2nd EARL OF LOVELACE — 1839–1906.

> Six lines of roman caps, centred: poor spacing of '& 13th …' Heraldry in low relief on one end, coloured. Rather an inadequate site for a rare tribute; moved into the church in 1941.
> R 12 × 25; 1907. (See also 169)

*122 Wall tablet to Major John SEYMOUR WYNNE-FINCH of Voelas and Cefn Amwlch at Tudweiliog Church, west of Pwllheli, Gwynedd, d.1906.

> The panel is shaped to suit the baroque design of the memorial by Caröe. Ten lines of massed caps with several joined letters and a large capital 'B' at the foot for 'Be of good courage and he shall strengthen thine heart'. Arms (by Caröe) in the strapwork cresting.
> R 17 × 32; 1907. (See 75A/P)

123 Tablet in St Andrew's, Roker, Sunderland, commemorating the building of the main fabric of the church, in 1906–1907, in memory of JANE PRIESTMAN.

> Seven lines of generous early caps and numerals – two letters joined and a smaller 'of' for spacing's sake, but some letters poorly cut, or perhaps re-cut by another hand.
> R 11 × 24; 1907. (See 123 A/P and B/P)

123A/P Tablet in the north porch of St Andrew's, Roker recording the grant of £200 by the Incorporated Church Building Society in 1907. 'Upon condition that all the seats are for the free use of the parishioners according to law.'

> Eight lines of lower case. c.1907. (See 123B/P)

123B/P Tablet in the south porch of St Andrew's, Roker, 'Whosoever thou art that enterest this church …'

> Perhaps the first of such tablets by E.G. with the inscription familiar on printed cards in church porches. This one has a Johnstonian touch in the flamboyant 'W' curving back to enclose a cross – and in the extended 't' to fill out the top line. c.1907. (The lettering on the mural in the chancel seems unlikely to be by E.G., possibly Macdonald Gill's?)

124 Bronze tablet for the Borough Polytechnic, Southwark, London.

> No trace of this now. 1907.

125 Inscription on a hogsback stone topped by a cross in Ryde Cemetery, Isle of Wight, in memory of IRENE NICHOLS, 1826–1907, elder daughter of Francis Morgan and Mary Nichols.

> This unusually fine inscription in relief has four lines of caps based on late medieval models with cut-away strokes. It is an early use by E.G. of a curved leg to the 'R'. (See 'Gill's R: a tailpiece' by James Mosley, in the *Monotype Recorder*, Autumn 1990.)

126 Tablet on a house said to be in Leamington, built for A. and M. Whitehorne.

  R 7 × 24; 1907.

127 Tablet at Woolwich in memory of General Sir HENRY AUGUSTUS SMYTH
  K.C.M.G., d.1906.

  It is likely this was destroyed in an air raid about 1940.
  R 42 × 19; 1907.

128 Tablet inside the porch of the Institute at Painswick, Stroud, Glos.: THE
  PAINSWICK INSTITUTE FOUNDED BY MRS MARY FRANCES SARAH
  WILLIAMS, 1906.

  R 7 × 26; 1907.

129 Six foundation stones for St John's Hospital, Morden Hill, Lewisham, S.E.13, of
  which the following is typical: 'This Porch was given In Memoriam R.M.C. 1907.'

  Assumed destroyed in an air raid about 1940.
  36 × 36; 1907.

130 Bronze tablet in St Martin's Church, Kensal Rise, London, in memory of Revd
  A. McLEAN HANLEY.

  1907.

*131 Inscription on wood for reredos in St John the Divine, Richmond, Surrey.

  Starting on the edge of the frame of a great triptych in large sixteenth-century caps (raised,
  concave and gilded) BEATI QVI DOMINO MORIVNTVR, the text continues across the
  altarpiece AGNVS DEI QVI TOLLIS PECCATA MUNDI MISERERE NOBIS, then below the
  right-hand frame TORCVLAR CALCAVI SOLVS. On the side panels there are Johnston's
  square dots, and a chalice and 'SJ' on one of the brackets. 1907. (See also 53 etc.)

*132 Memorial of Hopton-Wood stone, on the wall near the Oxford staircase, in the
  Ladies' College, Cheltenham, in memory of DOROTHEA BEALE, LL.D., 1831–
  1906, Principal of the College, 1858–1906.

  Macdonald Gill designed the elaborate border and the floral circle and ribbons at the top.
  The inscription by E.G. is magnificent, with many contrasting elements done with great
  authority – the name is incised, raised and gilded; red italic above; roman caps and lower
  case in red; green leaves, and surprisingly, a big 'O' for 'OF' with the 'F' in the middle; at
  the foot an interlaced colophon. There are several joined letters, a tall 'I', and in parts the
  spacing is fairly free. The admonitory text at the foot is in fine lower case 'DO not think of
  this life as discontinuous with the eternal ...' Small italic at the top, 'In loving thankful
  remembrance of ...'
  12 ft × 9 ft; c.1907.

133 Tablet inventoried as on the south side of the Lady Chapel of Gloucester
  Cathedral, in memory of DOROTHEA BEALE.

  This small memorial was included in error as by E.G., but is by Alfred Drury.

134 Oval memorial tablet stated as in St Bartholomew's Hospital, London – JACOBI
  ANDREW, fl.1897.

  c.1907.

A 9-ft high memorial in a grand setting, in memory of Dorothea Beale, Cheltenham Ladies College, c.1907 (132).

135 Alabaster tablet erected by the 2nd Battalion 'The Buffs' in memory of their
Colonel, EDGAR EVELYN RAVENHILL, D.S.O., who died at Wynberg, Cape
Colony, February 6, 1907.

> Fifteen lines of roman caps of two sizes, centred, very closely spaced and crowded into
> the frame, but D.S.O. very widely spaced for emphasis. Because WYNBERG offered a
> unique opportunity for a crafty signature, a tiny 'A' is cut before the ERG, and 'ILL 1908' is
> added.
> R 21 × 19; c.1907.

136 Inscription for a stone laid by Gertrude and Lawrence Squire.

> R 6 × 26; 1907.

137 Gravestone of red Mansfield stone, All Saints, Marple, Cheshire, surmounted by
a cross, the inscription in relief, in memory of THOMAS DOLLING BOLTON –
1841–1906.

> Done in collaboration with Macdonald Gill, hence the leafy design. Fine caps, raised, and
> good sculptural treatment with several monograms of chi-rho and I.H.C.
> R 21 × 25; c.1907.

138 Hopton-Wood stone tablet, the inscription in relief, in memory of GERTRUDE
EMILY CUNNINGHAM-FOOT, 1872–1899.

> The name spaciously set, the rest solid in six short lines; at the foot a fleur-de-lys, 'Inveni
> portum' and R.I.P., separated by E.G.'s square dots. Site unknown. c.1907.

139 Foundation stone in the Children's Ward of the Essex County Hospital,
Colchester: THIS WAS LAID WITH MASONIC CEREMONIAL BY COLONEL THE
RIGHT HONOURABLE MARK LOCKWOOD, P.C., C.V.O., M.P., GRAND MASTER
OF THE FREEMASONS OF ESSEX.

> A very mature work for its date, with distinguished lower case, and caps for the name.
> R 16 × 36; 1907. (cf 172)

140 Brass tablet for the entrance hall of the CENTRAL FOUNDATION GIRLS
SCHOOL, Spital Square, Bishopsgate, London E.1, recording the history of the
school.

> Though for brass, the lettering is all calligraphic in fifteen lines, with big initials, justified
> to the left, and big spaces to the right. The tablet is (twice) 'signed' with a cross and four
> dots. All very lively.
> R 19 × 45; c.1907. (See 146)

141 Tablet in memory of WILLIAM MAUNSELL REEVES of Ebbisham House,
Epsom, d.1907.

> Six lines of fine caps, but still no curve to the leg of the 'R'; unnecessarily narrow 'G' and
> 'C'.
> R 9 × 20; 1907.

142 Bronze tablet in Cape Town Cathedral in memory of FYDELL EDMUND
GARRETT, 1865–1907.

> Illustrated in Lawrence Weaver's Memorials and Monuments, 1915. Surmounted by a wreath
> below a camber-arched top, eighteen lines, with an eight-line verse in lower case, and

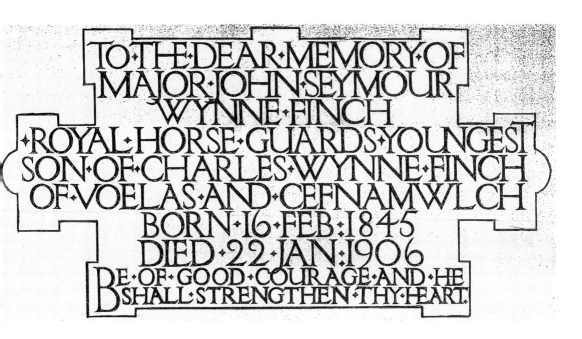

TO·THE·DEAR·MEMORY·OF
MAJOR·JOHN·SEYMOUR
WYNNE·FINCH
·ROYAL·HORSE·GUARDS·YOUNGEST
SON·OF·CHARLES·WYNNE·FINCH
OF·VOELAS·AND·CEFNAMWLCH
BORN·16·FEB·1845
DIED·22·JAN·1906
BE·OF·GOOD·COURAGE·AND·HE
SHALL·STRENGTHEN·THY·HEART·

24   Massed caps and
joined letters within a
strapwork memorial,
Pentrefoelas Church,
Gwynedd, 1907 (122).

AN

GRAF

KESSLER

MCMVIII

25   Carving on the lid of
an oak case for a
presentation address, 1908
(145).

finishing with a line of caps, 'He looked forward and made some beginnings ...'
Architect, Herbert Baker.
24 × 26; 1908.

143 Reredos at St Bartholomew and St Christopher, Haslemere. Below eight saints
in arched panels, and divided by octagonal oak columns: CHRISTVS VIN / CIT
CHRISTVS REGNAT CHR / ISTVS IMPERAT.

Bold raised and gilded caps with some letters freely joined; a tall 'I' for 'Imperat'.
Architect, Charles Spooner. 1908.

144 Stone tablet at St DUBRITIUS, LLANVACHES, Newport, Gwent, commemorating the restoration of the church by Godfrey Charles Morgan, 1st Viscount
Tredegar.

A calligraphic layout (understood to be by Macdonald Gill) with poor spacing; flourished
italic caps at the foot for names of rector and churchwardens.
R 12 × 19; c.1908. (See also 156)

145 Inscription: AN GRAF KESSLER MCMVIII on the upper of two boards (10 × 7)
intended for a case to contain a Memorial Address written on vellum by Edward
Johnston.

A poorly linked 'R' and 'A', but a bold and fine 'K'. The work is signed on the underside
of the upper board 'A. E. R. Gill carver', the 'R' with a cheerfully extended leg.
R 7 × 6; 1908.

146 Brass tablet for the Central Foundation Girls' School, Spital Square, Bishopsgate,
London, E.1, in memory of the Revd WILLIAM ROGERS, d.1896.

Six lines, and dates, centred, except the last line: a cross with four dots at the foot. The 'L'
of 'school' extends a long way à la Johnston (*Writing & Illuminating & Lettering* pp. 206 and
290).
R 9 × 26; 1908. (See 140)

147 Notice Board for KING'S COLLEGE HOSPITAL, Denmark Hill, London, S.E.5.

1908. (See also 182, 190 and 269)

148 Two panels formerly on either side of the fireplace in the Board Room, York
City & County Bank. Lettered Y.C. & C.B. and A.D.1908.

Possibly a brotherly collaboration, as Macdonald Gill's note reads 'The sides of the letters
are slightly bevelled (naturally) this bevel not only gives strength but enables greater
refinement of form to be carved – as sharp corners will not break off.' The ampersand
links well with the 'B', and raised dots characteristically fill the spaces. The 'D' of A.D. has
E.G.'s definite downward curve at the top. (Stored in St Saviour's Church, York, 1973.)
7 × 8; 1908. (See also note quoted in 151)

149 Tablet in memory of Colonel PERCY RALPH RICARDO, C.B., Commandant of
the Commonwealth Military Forces, Victoria, d.1907, buried at Melbourne,
Australia.

He served in South Africa during the Boer War in command of the Queensland Mounted
Rifles, a regiment he raised some years previously. Fourteen lines.
c. 28 × 17; 1908.

26　Panels for the York City and County Bank, 1908 (148).

150 Inscription on the font in St Mary's, Hornsey, London, the gift of Evan Hare, 1899.

> THE is joined twice as one form. There are small characteristic touches such as a small 'of' and a long head to an 'N'.
> R 11 × 16; 1908.

*150A/P Triptych memorial in an elaborate gilded frame (Architect, F.C. Eden) at Shifnal Church, Shropshire, in memory of REVD G. BOTSFIELD.

> The central panel has a blue background, and the lower-case lettering is raised in gesso and gilded. (About 3 in. of the inscription towards the foot is later work of the 1920s by another hand.) The side panels have painted texts in lower case, in black, with flowing red caps for certain words. At the foot of the right-hand panel is a typical four-dot cross with long one-sided serifs, like a 'crux ansata'. The left-hand panel has an encircled cross – and a floral pattern presumably by Macdonald Gill, to whom may also be attributed the painted outer sides of the panels. 1908.

151 Memorial panel on a granite boulder over a grave in Logie Coldstone Churchyard, near Dinnet, Grampian, in memory of GEORGE CHRISTOPHER CARTER, d.1907.

> A note on the drawing for raised letters in granite says 'This drawing is done in freehand to indicate that the panel is to be done freely and not mechanically. The ground between the letters is not to be quite flat (see section) it is to be rounded up (or 'pillowed' slightly). The fine points of the ends of the letters can easily be obtained if the letters are carved with a slight bevel as shown in section.' The 1⅛ in. letters are within a squared boundary reflecting the length of each word, with two cases of combined letters to save space – 'HR' and 'HE'. (G.C. Carter was the architectural assistant under whom E.G. worked in Caröe's office.)
> 9 × 11; 1908. (See also 148 note and 424)

152 Nameboard: WAYSIDE, in Cavendish Avenue, Cambridge.

> A painted inscription for the first house occupied by Sir Sydney Cockerell in Cambridge. 1908.

153 Inscription in relief, at Manchester College, Oxford in memory of author and journalist FRANCES POWER COBBE, 1822–1904, below a bas-relief portrait by Hope Pinker.

> A further inscription is below, about the presentation of the memorial to the College in 1908.
> R 4 × 16, 1908.

*154 Marble tablet in St Egwin's Church, Norton, near Evesham, in memory of MARY BEATRICE BOULTER, daughter of the Revd Walter Consitt Boulter, who died in 1902, in her 21st year.

> After the first three lines, the rest – until the last three – are justified to the left, small leafy fillers enlivening one line on the right, and a big 'S' on the left. More leaves at head and foot, and a rope moulding round it all. A very distinguished and characteristic work. (See Plate VI in the Inventory.)
> R 30 × 20; 1908.

MARY BEATRICE
only daughter
of Walter Consitt Boulter,
Vicar of this Parish, died 12 Mar.
1902, in her 21st. year. She was a student of the
Royal Academy of Arts
& Organist of this Church.
This window, patterned on
one formerly existing here,
together with the glass showing what things she loved,
was dedicated
in memory of her,
24 Feb. 1906.

27   *A characteristic early wall tablet in marble, St Egwin's Church, Norton, Worcs., 1908 (154).*

155 Headstone at St Mary's Church, St Mary's, Adelaide, South Australia, in memory of Revd WILLIAM SAMUEL MOORE, d.1900, Rector 1884–1900.

Seven lines of caps; one inexplicable tall 'I' in 'William'.
R 16 × 16; 1908.

156 Tablet in St Dubritius, Llanvaches, Newport, Gwent, for a screen erected in memory of ROSAMOND EMILY LINDSAY, d.1908.

One line of caps, seven of lower case; good typical space filling.
R 10 × 15; 1908. (See also 144)

157 Tombstone at St Paul's, Over Tabley, Knutsford, Cheshire, of HENRY LEWIS BROOKE LANGFORD-BROOKE, 1840–1907.

This unusually well-designed cross has a generously leaved panel (designed by Macdonald Gill) and a lettered panel below. The lettered panel (four lines of caps) bears a crest of a badger below the arched moulding. 'Well beloved' in italic.
32 × 23; 1908.

158 Portland memorial stone of JOHANNES PITT, 1806–1908, Chief Constable of the County of Sussex, 1880–1885. Also in memory of his wife ELIZABETH.

A design of three panels like 160 is in the St Bride Printing Library. Location of grave unknown.
Approx. 72 × 78; 1908.

159 Stone plaque commemorating the golden wedding of ANDREW AND CHARLOTTE JOHNSTON of Woodford Green, Essex.

An early example of a curved leg for the capital 'R'. (Andrew Johnston, M.P., J.P., was the uncle of Edward Johnston.)
R 16 × 21; 1908.

*160 Headstone of three panels (the centre one arched) in Hopton-Wood stone in Hanwell Cemetery, Middlesex in memory of NANCY ANNIE EMILY HEAL, 1881–1907.

This 7 ft-wide stone (100 yds north of the former chapel) is exceptional in several ways: the cornice is embellished with the leafy carvings (cf 112) familiar in E.G.'s engravings; the four bold engaged pilasters have interesting basket-capitals; the panels are topped by well-shaped mouldings, and the layout of the lettering on the centre panel is characteristically asymmetrical. (The later work on the left-hand panel is by another hand.) A leafy cross is carved within the arch. A splendid example of a memorial.
27 × 18; 1908.

161 Foundation stone for the Congregational Church, Charlton, Kent, laid by Revd S. Lloyd-Davies, Pastor, 29 October, 1908. Architects, Griffin and Woollard.

There are six such stones on the front of the church, including 163, the others laid by W. J. Ruffel, Revd J. Landel Jones, E. P. Williams J.P., and John Carter.
12 × 18; 1908.

162 Tombstone of JOHN BERRY of Westerbogie and Inverdovat-Tayfield, 1725–1817. And of JANET FRASER his wife, 1731–1762, ISABELLA LAW of Pitillock his

28   *A generous pilastered family grave memorial, Hanwell Cemetery, Middlesex, 1908 (160).*

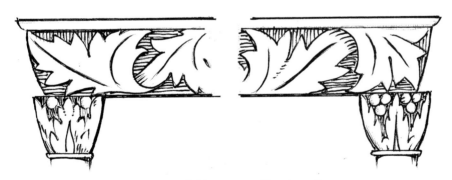

29   *Detail of the cornice moulding of no. 160.*

second wife, 1739–1807, MARGARET BERRY, 1781–1864, and SARAH
CRAWFURD BERRY, 1782–1880. Location unknown.

> 1908.

163 Foundation stone for the Congregational Church, Charlton, laid by the Revd
R. Fotheringham, Chairman, London Congregational Union, 1908.

> 12 × 18; 1908. (cf 161)

164 Painted letters: HEARTH, commissioned by the Earl of Lytton for Knebworth
House.

> The drawing shows a big 'H', a well-tailed 'R' and a leaf.
> 10 × 30; 1908.

165 The base of a marble bust and a pedestal at Eton, in memory of EDMOND
WARRE, C.B., C.V.O., Provost of Eton, 1884–1905.

> The base has four lines of gilt caps and a tiny shield (Eton College), and the pedestal five
> lines in black.
> R 7 × 7; 1908.

165A/P Cast bronze tablet in memory of Col. J. A. MAN-STUART C.B., C.M.G. 1844–
1908 at Banchory, Grampian with an enamelled shield by Macdonald Gill.

> Illustrated in Weaver's *Memorials and Monuments*. Italic at the foot.
> 29 × 10, c.1908.

166 Brass tablet in memory of SAMUEL NATHANIEL ELLIOT, d.1903.

> Part is centred, part justified to the left.
> R 10 × 19; c.1908.

167 Inscription above the entrance to Lodging Home for Working Women,
Portman House, 21 Harrow St, Lisson Grove, London, N.W.8; now demolished.

> This was one of the Shaftesbury Institutes, also known as Miss Meredith Brown's Homes.
> c.1908.

*168 Inscription on a monument at Kensal Green, London, in memory of WILLIAM
SMITH WILLIAMS, 1820–1906, and MARGARET ELIZABETH WILLIAMS, his
widow: 'Dying beloved with friends and happiness blessed ...' but the rest is
indecipherable.

> The four-sided stone also commemorates LOWES DICKINSON 1819–1908 'Full of noble
> device; of all sorts enchantingly beloved' and MARGARET ELLEN, his wife 1826–1882 (as
> shown in the *Burlington Magazine*, March 1910). The drawing for this monument showed
> shell-headed niches in mosaic and gilding, and a note, 'drip moulds to prevent water
> running down the gold' – but alas this embellishment was never done. Nonetheless it is a
> rare and distinguished memorial even in its decay.
> 1909. (See note under 88)

168A Hopton-Wood stone panel with alphabet of roman capitals, incised with 'V'
section.

> This was carved for Edward Johnston in April 1909 from which collotype reproductions

were made for his portfolio *Manuscript & Inscription Letters*, first published by John Hogg, London, September 1909, and later by Sir Isaac Pitman & Sons, Ltd. A reproduction was also published (1936) by the Victoria & Albert Museum as No. 1 of a series of four Lettering Sheets. Plaster casts of this panel (11 × 17) were sold by John Hogg, London. On the left – 'A. E. R. Gill, letter cutter'; on right 'C. Smith & Sons, Moulders.'
10 × 16; 1909.

168B Hopton-Wood stone panel with alphabet of lower-case italics and numerals.

One of three alphabets carved for Johnston in April 1909 (see 168A). This is Plate 14 of the portfolio and No. 2 of the Lettering Sheets. 1909.

168C Hopton-Wood stone panel with raised capitals and numerals.

The third of the three alphabets carved for Edward Johnston in April 1909 (see 168A and 168B). This was Plate 15 of the portfolio of *Manuscripts & Inscription Letters*. Plaster casts of this panel were sold by John Hogg, London, who published the portfolio, 1909.

169 Inscribed tablet in remembrance of Ralph, EARL OF LOVELACE, 1839–1906, for cottages the property of the Countess of Lovelace. Location unknown.

Rubbings show 3 in. caps apparently cut direct into stone over about 17 ft. 1909. (See also 21)

170 Inscription for brass plates: SWINBURNE, O'GORMAN & BAILLIE of 82 Victoria Street, London, S.W.1, 1909.

171 Cruciform headstone inventoried as for … ALWYN with foliage sculpture, and a blank shield on the drawing.

Presumably this relates to 268.
23 × 21; 1909.

172 Foundation stone for Wykeham Hall, Market Place, Romford, noted in the *Inventory* as 'Romford Institute': 'This stone was laid with masonic ceremonial by Colonel the Right Honourable MARK LOCKWOOD P.C., C.V.O., M.P. Grand Master of the Freemasons of Essex 1 May 1909 The Right Rev the Bishop of Colchester Vicar: E. Winmill & G. F. Daldy: Churchwardens.'

Cf 139 with similar wording in 1907. The names at the foot are treated very informally; the rest is centred. Distinguished even in its decrepit state.
36 × 24; 1909.

173 Headstone in memory of WILLIAM SHERWOOD, d. 1909.

A five-line inscription surmounted by a scrolly top with a bas-relief of two cherubs' heads; probably in an R.C. cemetery.
R 10 × 21; c.1909.

174 Panel inscribed with the names of the Clerks of the Peace of the North Riding of Yorkshire at Northallerton, over the fireplace in the Clerk's Office in County Hall.

In caps and lower case, this list is in three columns, with dates from 1543; but after 1916, the names are by another hand.
R 16 × 37; 1909.

30   *A generous early alphabet cut in Hopton-Wood stone, 1909 (168A).*

175 Inscription above a tap below a stone wall at Mells, Somerset: FOR THE USE OF MELLS VILLAGE IN MEMORY OF MARK HORNER 1908.

> The circle containing the inscription of seven lines of caps (with several letters joined) is between areas of guilloche carving; designed by Lutyens.
> 21 in. diam.; 1909.

175A/P Tombstone in Mells Churchyard, of Mark Horner d. 1908.

> In the form of a classical block by Lutyens. 1909.

176 Water house (or Memorial Well) designed by Lutyens, at Mells, Somerset, bearing an inscription: FOR THE USE OF MELLS VILLAGE IN MEMORY OF MARK HORNER 1908, as for the Memorial Tap (175).

> Cut in the stone round the inside just below the roof. 1908.

177 Tombstone in white marble in memory of SOPHIE L. A. KESSLER, born in Frankfurt-A-M., 1854, d. in London 1909.

> A free layout, evidently set out with wide pencil, surmounted by a bas-relief cross. The 'am Main' is expressed $\frac{A}{M}$.
> R 9 × 12; 1909.

178 Head- and footstones of Portland stone, at Broughty Ferry, Dundee, Tayside, in memory of ROSE TICHENER, 1880–1908.

> 1909.

179 Chronogram inscription: SCVTIFERI GENERI LVX VITAE LVCET ISTE TVTETVR VERE LIMINA NOSTRA DEUS for a lintel at 'Little Croft', Steventon, Abingdon, Berks., the residence of G. F. Squire.

> Each letter for making taller (providing the date in roman numerals) is marked on the drawing with a dot below. Apparently not used as a lintel but to record CVIII LVXVILVCII VVV LIMIDV…
> R 10 × 21; 1909.

180 Headstone in the City of London and Tower Hamlets Cemetery, Mile End Road, London, E.1, for grave No. T992. But no trace of this now. (A drawing, 10 × 12, is initialled by Macdonald Gill, 1909.)

181 Tablet of white marble on a black stone base in St Maelog, Llandyfaelog, Carmarthen, commemorating the ministry of the Revd PETER WILLIAMS, Annotator and Publisher of the Welsh Bible. Born at Westmarsh, Llansadurnen, 1723, died and buried at Llandyfaelog, 1796.

> The drawing shows 'Full-size setting out for a painted inscription'.
> 36 × 51; 1909.

182 Foundation stone for King's College Hospital, Denmark Hill, London, S.E.5, laid by King Edward VII. Architects, Colcutt and Hamp.

> E.G. notes 'about 1½ days work in it without colouring' (i.e. 57 letters at 12 hrs = 5 letters per hour). Apart from the long tail to the 'K', the layout on this stone is more than usually like an architect's layout, lining up five lines, centred, to a similar width.
> 21 × 24; 1909. (See also 147, 190 and 269)

1909

183 Foundation stones for Sutton Adult School, Sutton, Surrey, laid 21 July by Mrs
R.C.Henderson, Thomas Wall and R.C.Forster. Architects, Frederick Wheeler,
Son & Searle.

R 7 × 31, 12 × 28 and 18 × 29; 1909.

184 Wood carving in the porch of Holy Trinity, Wonston, Sutton Scotney, Hants.
Possibly a notice board. 1909.

185 Inscription in Mission Hall, Walworth, in memory of CHARLES HERMAN
PRIOR.

Plain caps, centred.
R 10 × 33; 1909.

186 Tablet in St John the Divine, Richmond, Surrey: WHOSOEVER THOU ART
THAT ENTEREST THIS CHURCH …

A fine calligraphic 'W'.
R 11 × 14; 1909.

187 Headstone in churchyard of St Mary, Storrington, Sussex, with a carving of a
chalice and paten in low relief surmounting the inscription, in memory of the
Revd GEORGE TYRRELL, d.July 1909.

R 26 × 23; 1909.

188 Tablet of incised letters in red (stated in the Inventory to be at St Lawrence, Over
Peover, Knutsford, Cheshire), in memory of MICHAEL FARRELL, d.1882 and of
his wife, d.1869.

A drawing shows a seven-line inscription within a camber-arched frame; a leafy
entablature and pilasters at the sides, to Michael Farrell 'of Davo' and his wife Anna
Looseley 1805–60. 'Both for many years members of this congregation.'
R 20 × 2; c.1909. (cf 197)

189 Memorial tablet for a window (stated in the Inventory to be at St Peter,
Llanwenarth Citra, Govilon, Abergavenny) in memory of HUGH BACKHOUSE
CHURCH, d.1909.

Caps and lower case centred: this appears to be in situ cutting.
R 14 × 23; 1909.

190 Inscriptions at King's College Hospital, Denmark Hill, London, S.E.5.

(Itemized also at 269) Large 'V'-cut caps, painted red NURSES' ENTRANCE above a long
arrow with six sharply cut flights. For certainty's sake, another arrow is just round the
corner. (See also 147, 182 and 269A–D). 1909.

190A/P At King's College Hospital: IN; MAIN ENTRANCE; OUT; GOODS
ENTRANCE; CASUALTIES; AMBULANCES; WAY IN.

1909. (See also 190)

191 Brass plate in memory of ROBERT CREIGHTON, d.1878, his wife and their
children, commemorating the gift of windows in a church.

One of the children referred to was Mandell Creighton (1843–1901), Bishop of Peterborough, 1891–97, and Bishop of London, 1897–1901. A good overall arrangement, filled out to the edge, and with the names in caps off-centre. Site unknown.
R 21 × 12; 1909.

192 Inscription in relief for a bust of JAMES MARTINEAU, 1805–1900, Professor of Philosophy, London University.

R 2 × 14; 1909.

193 Incised inscription: WHY MAKE YE THIS ADO ... AND WEEP THE DAMSEL IS NOT DEAD ...

A superb work – 4 in. Greek letters, 2 in. for the English. Location unknown.
R 31 × 48; c.1909.

194 Hopton-Wood stone tablet in a chapel in St Wulfran's, Ovingdean, near Brighton, commemorating the erection of the chapel, by Arthur Carey, of Downside, Roedean, in 1907. 'Blessed be God the father of all mercies and the God of all comfort.' 2 Cor. 1. 7.

This is on the foundation of a Norman Chantry destroyed by fire in 1377. A simple yet outstanding example of E.G.'s layout. Generous caps and the date in red; the rest in exemplary lower case; and the text in italic with a cheerful 'B' and 'F'. All encased in a simple moulding.
15 × 33; 1909.

195 Stone tablet: NORTHEND for a farm house at North Moreton, Didcot, occupied by the Boulter family in 1909, later named 'Cherry Court'.

c.1909. (cf 154)

196 Inscription for reredos presented in memory of JOHN THOMAS ATKINSON, of Hillfield, Selby, Yorks., d.1909.

Calligraphic pen lettering.
R 3½ × 5; c.1909.

197 Tablet in memory of ALFRED HERBERT WILLIAM FARRELL of Davo, d.1909, and of his wife and children.

(Not, as stated in the Inventory, at Over Peover, Cheshire.) This would appear to be an important work: seventeen lines commemorating six members of the family, and topped by a cambered cornice with leafy bas-relief carving. At the side are pilasters with capitals of a thistle and a rose. c.1909. (cf 188)

198 Poster for KEYMER & DISTRICT LAND CLUB – this used to meet at the Bull public house, Ditchling. Caps, lower case and italic.

2¼ in. caps painted for 'OPEN AIR MEETING'; very lively. c.1910.

199 In the Inventory as a headstone of HOPE BROWN, wife of Alexander Easton Gibb of Kew & Rosyth, d.1909.

Though described thus, her memorial of classical design in Richmond Cemetery would not seem to be by E.G. A rubbing (12 × 15) for a stone shows seven lines of caps, the 'R's swashed out at the foot. This is on a relief of a mother and child with toy bricks (Gibb was an engineer) against a classical arched background. 1910.

200 Gravestone of Hopton-Wood stone with inscription surmounted by a large bas-relief crucifix at St Egwin's, Norton, near Evesham, in memory of HANNAH MARIA BOULTER, d.1909.

> The figure is within a shallow cross defined by a moulding, and has JESU MERCY below in raised letters. The memorial is within a moulded frame at the foot with carved corbels. The 'R' of BORN is well flourished out to fill the space at the end of the next line. 1910.
>
> (Carved between February and April 1910, the crucifix bears a close comparison with the crucifix in the Tate Gallery (203), also of 1910.)

201 Foundation stone for St Jude-on-the-Hill, Hampstead Garden Suburb, London, N.W.11, laid by the Hon. W.F.D.Smith P.C. 'on the feast of St Mark E.M. 25 April, 1910'. Architect, Edwin Lutyens.

> AMDG above, and a long leg to the 'R' of 'April'.
> 19 × 33; 1910.

201A/P A similar stone laid by the Earl of Crewe K.G. in the Lady Chapel.

> Freely done. 1910.

201B/P A similar stone recording the gift of the site of the church, the cutting of the first sod, and the appointment of the first vicar.

> c.1910.

202 Hopton-Wood stone tablet for the wall of a seaside house.

> This represents a woman in a crouching position supporting the tablet which is inscribed in Greek, ΕΣΤΙΝ ΘΑΛΑΣΣΑ ΤΙΣ ΔΕ ΝΙΝ ΣΒΕ ΣΕΙ. 'There is the sea, and who shall drain it dry?' from *Agamemnon*, by Aeschylus. One of E.G.'s earliest carvings, first exhibited at the Chenil Gallery, Chelsea, in January 1911.
> R 5 × 7; 1910.

203 Hopton-wood stone relief of a 'T'-shaped Crucifix depicting a nude Christ, with the words NEC IN TIBIIS VERI BENE PLACITUM ERIT EI (Psalm 147.10) incised vertically on the cross-shaft. On either side is inscribed in raised Greek caps, massed, ΚΑΙΕΙΣΙΝ ΕΥΝΟΥΧΟΙ ΟΙΤΙΝΕΣ. 'And there be eunuchs' (St Matthew, 19.12)

> The Greek lettering bears a strong resemblance to the bold form E.G. used at Ilkley in 1904 (40) but with a fine swing to the chi in the Tate example. First exhibited at the Chenil Gallery, in January 1911, and presented to the Tate Gallery by the Contemporary Art Society in 1920.
> 37 × 31; 1910. (cf 200 and 203A)

203A A ROLAND FOR AN OLIVER. Hopton-Wood stone relief of a panel depicting a nude female figure with words from Swinburne's *Hymn to Proserpine*: O PALE GALILEAN, BUT THESE THOU SHALT NOT TAKE: THE LAUREL THE PALM & THE PAEAN THE BREASTS OF THE NYMPHS IN THE BRAKE ... inscribed round a rectangle, the lowest part upside down.

> First exhibited as a companion piece to the *Crucifixion* (203) and exhibited at the Chenil Gallery in January 1911. The title *A Roland for an Oliver* was that given to the work in the

catalogue of the exhibition. It was purchased by the Contemporary Art Society, and presented to the Tate Gallery. E.G. wrote to his brother Vernon, 'They are a pair – one being a symbol of renunciation and the other a symbol of acceptance.'
R 37 × 27; 1910.

204 Wall tablet at St Mary's, Hadleigh, Suffolk, commemorating the gift of an altar and ornaments in memory of ANNA FRANCES SPOONER, 1830–1906.

Characteristically the names are boldly in caps and placed asymmetrically, and the lowest line in italic. There is an ambiguity in the statement that in memory of Mrs Spooner, the second wife of the former Rector, the gifts were made by 'some of his relations who loved her' ...
R 12 × 19; c.1910.

205 Monument stated in the *Inventory* as at Haslemere, with allegorical figure and inscription: IN MEMORIAM M.E.D[AKYNS] JAN III MCMVIII ...

E.G.'s drawing for this monument bears the inscription: 'The body springs from the grave, the soul descends from an opening cloud; they rush together with inconceivable energy: they meet never again to part.' (Text to illustration in Blake's *Grave*, p.82.) Another sketch, a different design, shows a carving of Mother and Child set within a recess. 1910.

206 Letters: HEATHCOTE, carved on the wall at the entrance of a house at Ilkley, Yorks., designed by Lutyens.

4 × 32; 1910.

207 Foundation stone for a house in Boys' Garden City, Woodford Green, Essex, laid in memory of Dr THOMAS JOHN BARNARDO (1845–1905), founder of the philanthropic institutions which bear his name.

This has the usual off-centre arrangement of caps.
c.9 × 18; 1910. (See also 208 and 209)

208 Foundation stone for a house in Boys' Garden City, Woodford Green, Essex, erected in memory of KING EDWARD VII and laid by Princess Alexander of Teck, 1910.

There is a new tendency here to give caps for emphasis of some words, somewhat arbitrarily chosen. Unusually, this six-line inscription is centred.
9 × 18; 1910. (See also 207 and 209)

209 Foundation stone for a house in Boys' Garden City, Woodford Green, Essex, 1910 in memory of Canon FLEMING.

Strong arbitrary caps for certain words; a centred text with a nice contrast by using italic in line 5.
9 × 18; 1910. (See also 207 and 208)

210 Stone inscription on a corbel in the hall of a house, Conduit Head, Cambridge, reading: FRANCIS DARWIN BUILT THIS HOUSE FOR FRANCIS & FRANCES CORNFORD 1910. (See also 371)

Four lines of small caps, the date large; joined letters TH and ND.
6 × 9; 1910.

210A/P CONDUIT HEAD carved on the beam of the porch of the front door of the same house.

> Grand 4½ in. caps spaced over 6 ft. 1910. (See also 371)

211 Tablet inscribed: THE DOVES BINDERY / MDCCCXCIII / THE DOVES PRESS / T.J. MCM C-S.

> Established first as 'The Doves Bindery' at 15 Upper Mall, Hammersmith, and later (c.1908) at 1 The Terrace, Hammersmith as 'The Doves Press', where it continued to flourish until 1916. The italic initials in the inscription relate to T.J. Cobden-Sanderson. (See Plate VII in the *Inventory*.)
> R 12 × 22; 1910.

212 Tablet in Hopton-Wood stone commemorating the restoration of ST ANDREW'S CHURCH, Tredunnoc, Usk, Monmouth.

> The date is shown in bas-relief in the cross at the top.
> 16 × 18; c.1910.

213 Foundation stone for Parish Hall, St John the Divine, Richmond, Surrey, laid by Viscount Halifax, 10 February 1911.

> This is 'V'-cut in the jamb beside the door. But above, on either side, is cut in relief caps the words 'St John's / Parish Hall'. These letters, and the 'St J' in the keystone have so close an affinity to E.G.'s work in the church that – though they are very un-Johnston, and not characteristic of E.G.'s work generally – they may be attributed to him. Can he also have carved the sumptuous leafy arch above? Or could this be by Macdonald Gill?
> R 12 × 23; 1910. (See also 53 etc.)

214 Portland headstone in Heene Cemetery, Worthing, Sussex in memory of CECIL EDGAR FISH, d.1910.

> Topped with a rambler rose in bas-relief.
> 60 × 30; 1911.

215 Inscription on Hopton-Wood stone: IF IT IS MORE BLESSED / TO GIVE THAN TO RECEIVE / IT IS MORE BLESSED TO / RECEIVE THAN TO REJECT. An exhibition piece.

> Exhibited at the Alpine Club Gallery, May 1918. Later in the collection of Ernest W. Porter, Derby.
> 11 × 20; 1910.

216 Inscription in memory of MARJORIE STEELE, d.1910.

> R 18 × 15; c.1910.

217 Inscription (from Goethe) on marble: OB NICHT NATUR / ZULETZT SICH / DOCH ERGRUNDE, the letters painted red.

> Presented to Edward Johnston, subsequently in the collection of A.E. Stiff. A free translation might run: 'Perhaps Nature may at last reveal her secrets.'
> 6 × 14; c.1910.

217A/P Monogram of J.G. carved on the lid of a sewing box.

> Made for Joanna Gill and surrounded by four dots.
> 3 × 2; c.1910.

218 Inscription in memory of General Sir HENRY ERRINGTON LONGDEN, K.C.B., C.S.I. – 1819–1890, who died at Bournemouth.

> A fine inscription, thirteen lines of caps, lower case and italic, part centred and part justified to the left; topped by a regimental badge with good ribbons for 'Lincolnshire Regiment' and the sphinx and EGYPT within an arch. Much about a battle, a siege and various actions. Site not known.
> R 22 × 31; c.1910.

219 Altar tomb in St Mary's Roman Catholic Cemetery, Kensal Green, London, of the poet FRANCIS THOMPSON, 1859–1907.

> The end panel is now somewhat obscured, 'Look for me in the nurseries of heaven' – from *To my godchild*. The 'of' has a fine long 'f'. On each side of the tomb chest is a wreath, and a cross on top, over all. E.G.'s drawing shows fine detail of mouldings.
> R 17 × 17; 1911. (See also 243)

*220 Granite foundation stone of the British Museum King Edward VII Galleries, in Montague Place, Bloomsbury.

> Presumably carved in situ, on three large stones over the door. The stone bears four lines of caps in which KING EDWARD THE SEVENTH'S GALLERIES spans the full width: then, small, 'This stone was laid by' followed by HIS MAJESTY KING EDWARD THE SEVENTH and 'on the twenty seventh day of June in the seventh year of his reign'. E.G. always made the most of a text to suit its position. Below on the stones beside the keystone of the door is carved ANNO DNI MCMVII, with the 'A' and 'D' very large. Architect, John Burnet. (The sketch at 1-inch scale was signed by E.G., 16 Old Buildings, Lincoln's Inn, April 1911, but the work was not carried out as shown.) 1911. (See also 394)

221 Ledgerstone with inscription and coat of arms, in the crypt of St Paul's Cathedral, in memory of WILLIAM HOLMAN HUNT, O.M., Painter, 1827–1910.

> A very fine coat of arms in relief within a roundel (one of four designs submitted, seven prepared), now rather worn. (A letter from the College of Arms reads 'Sir, your design is correct and very beautiful, Yours faithfully, Everard Green, Rouge Dragon'.) Thirteen lines – and 'Their bodies are buried in peace but their fame liveth for evermore: UT MORIENTES ET ECCE VIVIMUS.' 1911.

222 Portland headstone in the Extra-Mural Cemetery, Brighton, in memory of SIR THOMAS EKINS FULLER K.C.M.G., 1831–1910.

> Topped by a leafy cornice, cambered in the centre, similar to the Heal memorial at Hanwell (160) with slender pilasters at the side, the text is within a shallow raised frame.
> R 20 × 24; 1911.

223 Memorial cross in the private graveyard at Wykeham Abbey, Scarborough, in memory of CECILIA MARY CHARLOTTE DOWNE, 1838–1910, wife of Hugh Richard, 8th Viscount Downe.

> This cross, on a battered plinth, as detailed by E.G. in interlacing Celtic fashion, has the shaft and arms tapering in his usual way. 'Note: cross to have a lead damp course provided by the Estate Clerk of Works.' 1911.

224 Brass plate in the Trinity Chapel at Canterbury Cathedral recording the recovery and replacement of ancient glass, in memory of ANNIE MOORE, d. December 1906.

> 5 × 8; 1911.

225 Foundation stone for the Psychological Laboratory, Cambridge, laid in 1911 by Esther, wife of WOLF MYERS, in whose memory the greater part of the building was provided by his family and friends. (In the Physiology Dept, Downing St.)

> To say the least, this is not like any other work by E.G., but there is a full-size setting-out, 22 × 18, signed by E.G. The rubbing 20 × 17 is endorsed: 'Supposed to be a copy of my drawing! A very decent piece of lettering but scarcely like the copy. E.G.' 1911.

226 Pedestal of grey Roman stone for bronze sundial with inscriptions on all four sides, in the churchyard St Margaret, Ditchling, erected to commemorate the coronation of King George V.

S SIDE (Crown)	E SIDE	N SIDE (Cross)	W SIDE
ERECTED IN	THIS DIAL	THIS CHURCH	ALFRED
COMMEMOR-	WAS ORIG-	DEDICATED	THE GREAT
ATION OF THE	INALLY IN	TO SAINT	LORD OF
CORONATION	THE GAR-	MARGARET	THE MANOR
OF KING	DEN OF THE	C A.D. 901	A.D. 871
GEORGE V	RANGER'S		
57th MONARCH	HOUSE IN		
OF ENGLAND	THE ROYAL		
A.D. 1911	PARK		

> Four instances of joined letters for THE, and in three different ways. 1911.

227 Inscription for beams: BUILT AT THE INSTANCE OF H. T. ANGELL.

> 1911.

228 Headstone of Hopton-Wood stone in Kenilworth Churchyard in memory of EDWARD HERBERT DRAPER 1841–1911, Clerk to the Guild or Fraternity of the Body of Christ of the Skinners of the City of London.

> Roman caps, lower case and italic; unusually, part justified to the right.
> R 22 × 22; 1912.

229 Incised tablet of Hopton-Wood stone in Hampstead in memory of OSCAR GUTTMANN, d. August 1910.

> Three roses within the arched top.
> 24 × 15; 1911.

230 Portland headstone surmounted by a cross within foliage, St John the Evangelist, Holdenhurst, Bournemouth, Hants, in memory of GERALD PEEL 1847–1910.

> With a fine epitaph in lower-case roman; a later inscription for his widow. A very distinguished stone.
> R 20 × 26; 1911. (See also 705A)

231 Inscription and emblem incised on Hopton-Wood stone: ΙΧΘΥΣ.

> R 7 × 8; c.1911.

232 Portland headstone (in the Inventory as being in the churchyard, St Simon and St Jude, Eastdean, Eastbourne) in memory of ANTHONY GEORGE NEW, 1870–1911.

> The inscription, unusually, is centred within a recessed and arched panel.
> R 21 × 17; 1912.

233 Bronze tablet on a marble background in Balliol College Chapel, Oxford, in memory of EDWARD CAIRD, 1835–1908, Master of Balliol 1893–1907.

> Thirteen lines of caps and lower case followed by five lines of lower-case Greek, all within a simple moulded frame with a camber arch. A very distinguished work, the effect slightly diminished by having the bronze to Dr Strachan-Davidson adjoining. The comparison of the spacing in each is instructive: Caird's lively, the other dead.
> 33 × 25; 1911. (See also 416A/P and 516)

234 Gravestone at St Mary's, Teddington, of STEPHEN HALES, D.D., F.R.S., Clerk of the Closet to the Princess of Wales, Minister of St Mary's Teddington for fifty-one years, d.1761.

> The gift of certain botanists, this replaces one that had become partly obliterated. (There is also a monument to Hales in Westminster Abbey.) A good example of mixed letter forms, and an especially fine italic.
> R 19 × 28; 1911.

235 Gravestone in churchyard of Our Lady of Consolation, West Grinstead, Horsham, Sussex, in memory of ISABELLA MARY COWIE, 1846–1903, also of ELLEN COWIE, 1851–1906.

> There is a curiously joined '3' and capital 'F', and the 'I' of Isabella goes, unusually, above and below the line: Johnstonian dots at the end of line 3 fill this space.
> R 21 × 28; 1911.

236 Hopton-Wood stone on grave in Brookwood Cemetery, Woking, of LINDSEY FORSTER BATTEN, d.1865 and NORMAN GOTTFRIED BATTEN, d.1873.

> Five lines of good simple italic, on a slightly rounded ('pillowed') surface.
> 9 × 24; 1911.

237 Inscription in Greek, set out in an ellipse: ΑΡΙΣΤΟΣ. ΙΑΤΡΟΣ ΚΑΙ ΦΙΛΟΣΟΦΟΣ – 'An excellent doctor and philosopher'. (cf 227 with 'C' as sigma.)

> R 13 × 18; c.1911.

237A/P Raised alphabet and numerals and (large) TAX AD in Hopton-Wood.

> Sections of three kinds of letter are shown. (See also *Writing & Illuminating & Lettering*, fig. 217 for sections of letters for large work and gilding.) 1911.

238 Memorial (in the *Inventory* as at Barn Hill Cemetery, Broughty Ferry, Dundee, Tayside) in memory of JOHN OGILVIE of Westlands, Broughty Ferry, 1831–1911.

> The drawing shows a tall pedimented stone, panelled on all sides. c.1911.

239 Tablet of Hopton-Wood stone in Teffont Evias Church, near Salisbury, in memory of ELLEN FLORA KEATINGE, 'Lady of the Manor of Teffont Ewyas', d.1907. Also of MAURICE KEATINGE, d.1896.

> Nineteen lines of good roman lettering.
> 35 × 21; 1912.

240 A four-line inscription of: MAKE THEM TO BE NUMBERED WITH THY SAINTS.

To get the spacing of the roman caps within the squarish stone there are tall 'T's in 'them' and 'with'.

R 15 × 17; c.1912.

241 Tablet of Hopton-Wood stone in Teffont Evias Church, near Salisbury, in memory of MARGARET HELEN MAYNE, d.1905. 'The last of the name of Mayne to inherit the manor of Teffont Ewyas ... buried beneath the tower of this church.'

Roman caps, centred, and a very odd figure 5.

R 12 × 25; 1912.

242 Inscription round four sides of a sundial of Portland stone for Neil Lyons, at Wivelsfield, Sussex: FULL MANY A GLORIOUS MORNING HAVE I SEEN ...

R 12 × 12; 1912.

243 Tablet of Hopton-Wood stone in Manchester University, in memory of FRANCIS THOMPSON, poet, 1859–1907. Student of Owens College 1877–1884.

Whatso looks lovelily

Is but the rainbow on life's weeping rain.

Why have we longings of immortal pain,

And all we long for mortal? Woe is me,

And all our chants but chaplet some decay,

As mine this vanishing – nay, vanished day.

The verse in a fine italic with a flowing 'W'. (Illustrated in Weaver's *Memorials and Monuments*.) 1912. (See also 219)

244 Tall Celtic cross of Green Borrowdale stone with interlaced ornament in memory of ISABELLA, widow of John Elliott Huxtable, d.1909.

The memorial includes the lamb and flag, a fish and a bell, and has an affinity with the Ilkley cross (40). There are five pencil drawings (coloured) for this, and a full-size sketch of the cross signed by E.G. 30.3.12 and revised 2 May. Location unknown.

R 27 × 8; 1912.

245 Brass plate relating to the clock in the church tower, St James the Great, Silsoe, Bedford, 'in commemoration of the visit of our late beloved King Edward VII to Wrest Park, when he was present at Divine Service, and contributed to the Offertory inaugurating the Fund on Sunday July 25 1909.'

A fine long tail to the 'K'.

R 20 × 13; 1912.

246 Cruciform headstone and footstone of Portland stone in Keymer Cemetery, Sussex, in memory of FREDERICK THOMAS RICHARD WHITE, 1896–1911.

R 14 × 18; 1912.

246A/P Inscription on three sides of the base of a statue of the Mother and Child, commissioned in 1912 by Dr Geoffrey Keynes (later Sir Geoffrey), in 1½ in. caps, arranged thus:

| ESURIENTES | IMPLEVIT | BONIS ET |
| DIVITES | DIMISIT | INANES |

Though this text from the Magnificat is meant to be read line by line (He hath filled the hungry with good things / The rich he hath sent empty away), E.G.'s arrangement gives a nice affinity to the verbs placed centrally. There are three joined letters; the leg of the 'R' curves out from the bowl. 1912.

247 Stone tablet in the Prefects' room, Godolphin School, Salisbury, commemorating the gift, by past and present pupils and their mistresses, of a museum to honour the memory of ETHEL EMMELINE JONES and her twenty-one years of service to the school.

Nine lines of roman caps with the dates in roman numerals. E.G.'s note on the detail layout says 'NB. Lines to be spaced out so as to come equal in length.'
11 × 27; 1912.

247A/P Sign carved in relief for the CAVE OF THE CALF, now destroyed.

The 'A' and 'V' were joined and the 'TH' and 'E' were one. This was probably part of E.G.'s work for Madame Strindberg's Cave of the Golden Calf cabaret club in Heddon Street, London W.1. 1912.

248 Memorial of Portland stone (stated in the *Inventory* as at Barn Hill Cemetery, Broughty Ferry, Dundee, Tayside) in memory of GEORGE OGILVIE, 1851–1912.

The design shows engaged columns with criss-cross relief carving, and a boldly arched cornice over the name etc: and the lower part as virtually a plinth composed of five lines of lettering spanning the width. (See Weaver's *Memorials and Monuments*, 1915.)
R 12½ × 22; 1912.

249 Headstone in Green Honister slate at Rickerby, near Carlisle, in memory of PRISCILLA HANNAH JOHNSTON, d.1912.

Simple arch-topped stone with roman and italic, and 'I will remember my covenant which is between me and you and every living creature.'
26 × 31; 1912.

250 Tall, narrow headstone of Hopton-Wood stone in churchyard of St Egwin's, Evesham, in memory of WALTER CONSITT BOULTER, 1848–1912.

At the top within a framed cross is a bas-relief of the dove and a chalice, which in turn surmounts a small crucifix, set within three lines of caps (AGNUS DEI QUI ...) with a well-tailed 'Q' in 'Requiem'. Below this, central on the shaft, is the memorial lettering within a raised moulded frame on corbels.
R 15 × 13; 1913.

251 Headstone of Hopton-Wood stone in the Jewish Cemetery, Necropolis Road, Bradford, in memory of BERTHA, wife of Moritz Rothenstein, 1844–1912. An additional inscription commemorates MORITZ ROTHENSTEIN, 1838–1914. Parents of Sir William Rothenstein, Albert Rutherston and Charles Rutherston. (See also 511)

At the top is a bas-relief portrait; within the italic a capital 'R'.
12 × 16; 1912, and 10 × 16; c.1914.

252 Tablet of Hopton-Wood stone in St Andrew's, Steyning, Sussex, recording the removal of galleries, etc., in memory of ARTHUR CONGREVE PRIDGEON, vicar, 1882–1907.

Cut by E.G. himself.
R 14 × 27; 1912.

31   Caps of two sizes, grandly disposed, at the British Museum Edward VII Galleries, 1911 (220).

32   Unity and diversity of sculptured symbols and lettering, St Egwin's, Norton, Worcs., 1913 (250).

AGNUS·DEI QUI·TOLLIS
PECCATA· MUNDI +
DONA·EI· REQUIEM

WALTER CONSITT
BOULTER
+ PRIEST +
VICAR OF NORTON
AND LENCHWICK
FROM 1891 TO 1902
BORN 22 JAN.1848
DIED 5 FEB.1912

253 Ledgerstone of Stancliffe stone at St John's, Dormansland, near Lingfield, Surrey, in memory of SYBIL GWENDOLINE SPENDER CLAY, 1910–1912 – 'God bless thee and keep thee, dear child'.

> At the top a bold cross within floral squares, below this a pair of clasped hands.
> R 19 × 14; 1912.

254 Tablet of white marble with leaded letters, in a niche at Manchester Crematorium (Southern Cemetery), in memory of JOHN TREGO GILL (E.G.'s uncle) 1847–1912.

> R 8 × 15; 1912.

255 Inscription on the tomb of OSCAR WILDE, in Père Lachaise Cemetery, Paris, carved by Jacob Epstein; now a national monument.

> The inscription is on the middle stone of the back of the memorial.
> 40 × 56; 1912.

256 Hopton-Wood stone tablet placed by the Ancient Order of Druids at Southdown Lodge, Hassocks, Sussex, to commemorate the planting of a tree to mark the coronation of King George V, 22 June, 1911.

> R 10 × 20; 1912.

257 Cross in churchyard of St Nicholas, Guildford, in memory of SYDNEY MELVILLE, widow of Joseph Spender Clay, wife of Beresford V. Melville, d.1912.

> The arms of the cross chamfered, with DENIQVE COELVM in 2 in. caps; unusually, roman caps on the base, as for Spender Clay (253). 1912.

258 Wall tablet for WORTH MANOR HOUSE, Worth, nr Crawley, Sussex, the home of Wilfred Scawen Blunt, 'Lord of the Manor, architect'.

> The tablet records the names of the builders, carpenters and labourers, etc.
> R 35 × 23; 1912.

259 Tablet of Hopton-Wood stone in St Mary's School, Ealing, in memory of Dame JANE RAWLINSON, who founded and endowed the school in 1712.

> R 22 × 24; 1912.

260 Memorial of Hopton-Wood stone in St Nicholas, Cranleigh, Surrey, in memory of AMY BONHAM, d.1910, with an inscription: I TRUST I DO NOT DISPLEASE GOD. FOR WHEN I REMEMBER OF THE BEAUTY AND OF THE NOBLESSE … followed by: Her Mother and Feb. 18, 1910.

> R 8 × 19; 1912.

261 Inscriptions on the stone base of a bronze statue of Capt. James Cook, 1728–1779 by John Tweed in the People's Park, West Cliff, Whitby, Yorks.

> A resounding text in 1½ in. caps in typical E.G. style: 'For the lasting memory of a great Yorkshire seaman this bronze has been cast & is left in the keeping of Whitby, the birthplace of those good ships that bore him on his enterprises, brought him to glory & left him at rest.'
> R 10 × 20, 28 × 17, 9 × 17; 1912.

262 Tablet, with inscription in Latin, in St John the Divine, Richmond, Surrey, in memory of MAUD WITHERS, d.1911.

> R 11 × 12; 1912. (See also 53 etc.)

263 Inscription on base of a statue of the Virgin Mary at Radley School: TU AD LIBERANDUM SUSCEPTURUS HOMINEM NON HORRUISTI VIRGINIS UTERUM.

> R 14 × 16; 1912.

264 Marble urn at Golders Green Crematorium in memory of ELBERT JAN VAN WISSELINGH, 1848–1912.

> R 5 × 10; 1913.

265 Bronze tablet for the Nicholson Ward for the Royal Alexandra Children's Hospital, Brighton, in memory of Major S. NICHOLSON, d.1912.

> Fine caps for 'To the Glory of God and the relief of his suffering children ...' then three lines of lower case carefully disposing the words to fill out to the ends of the lines; engraved, and filled in red and black.
> R 8 × 38; 1913.

266 Hopton-Wood stone tablet, Holy Trinity, Sloane Street, London, recording the gift of the reredos (the work of John Tweed – cf 261) in memory of JOHN ROSS, 1859–1905.

> Twelve lines of inscription, placed on the back of the reredos and hard to see. It has boldly sited off-centre caps.
> 26 × 35; 1913. (See also 10)

*267 Table tomb of Portland stone at Holy Trinity, Calne, Wilts., with a coat of arms in memory of Sir CHARLES HENRY STUART RICH, Fourth Baronet of Shirley, FSA, d.1913.

> The details of mouldings are typical, as also the squat pilasters. On the side, in generous caps, the words are well chosen to fill out the space. On one end 'In God's keeping'; and on the other the impaled arms canted, and surmounted by a small helm with a very simple, long mantle (scarcely a mantling) and a wyvern crest. The motto ribbon is boldly placed to extend on each side of the helm. All is in relief within a deep recess. 1913.

268 Headstone in churchyard of St Nicholas, Sevenoaks, Kent, in memory of CHARLES HERBERT AYLWIN, d.1909, and of his daughter KATHLEEN MABEL GRACE MOORE, d.1911.

> The head of the stone is 'corbie-stepped' and responds to a cross shape surrounding leaves and a fine shield and crest.
> R 11 × 22; 1913. (cf 171)

269A & B King's College Hospital, Denmark Hill, London, S.E.5. Letters 6 in. high for the floors, and at the entrance to the wards.

> These were designed ½ in. deep for setting in ¾ in. asphalt, thus without long serifs. The freehand drawing has great authority. The fixing details for the letters for the floor require 'Bar to be soldered to upper face of letters to strengthen them if necessary' i.e., when reversed, to anchor into asphalt. 1913.

269C Carved lettering in King's College Hospital in caps on piers and walls – Main Entrance; IN and OUT; Patients' Entrance; Outpatients' Entrance; Nurses' Entrance; Goods Entrance; Casualties; Ambulances; Ambulances Way In.

All are well integrated with the architecture; some have arrows.

269D Inscription recording the opening by King George V, July 26, 1913.

This is similar to the foundation stone laid by Edward VII in 1909, with a similar extended leg for the 'K' (182). Architects, Colcutt and Hamp.
R 22 × 24; 1913. (See also 147, 182, 190, 190A/P)

270 Grave kerbing (for a cross with lettering not by E.G.) in Ditchling churchyard, in memory of RICHARD LINGARD STOKES, d.1912. 'This kerb is placed here in token of affection and respect by many patients and friends in Ditchling and its neighbourhood.'

R 17 × 52; 1913.

271 Holy Water stoups of polished Hopton-Wood stone commissioned by Wilfred Meynell with inscriptions IN NOMINE PATRIS ...

There are rubbings of five different designs or layouts. 1913.

272 Incised inscription (letters in red) on tablet in the Deaf and Dumb Institute, Kemp Town, Brighton: BOYS' RECREATION ROOM, HUGH S. HEAL MEMORIAL, 1913.

R 11 × 19; 1913.

273 Tablet inscribed: OMNIA PER IPSUM ET SINE IPSO NIHIL.

This tablet was given by E.G. to his father for his birthday, 30 September 1913. Later in the possession of E.G.'s nephew, John Skelton.
6 × 9; 1913.

273A Lines from Tennyson's *The Lotus Eaters*: LET THERE BE MUSIC HERE ... for a panel over the fireplace in the music room at Leasam House, Playden, Rye, Sussex. With floral emblems (coloured) executed by E.G.'s brother Macdonald Gill, 1914.

This was commissioned by Lady Maud Warrender who lived there. The house was sold to the Sussex County Council in 1946.
19 × 66; 1913.

273B Portland headstone at Birchington, Kent, in memory of BRIAN CHAMBREY TOWNSHEND – 1874–1913.

This has E.G.'s special pilasters, cross-banded and an arched cornice, enclosing the City of London arms. The inscription ends 'His later career was marred by illness but he lived in the lives of his friends and lives still in their hearts'. On the base is cut 'Have you heard that it was good to gain the day? I also say it is good to fall – battles are lost in the same spirit in which they are won'.
R 37 × 30; 1914.

274 Wall tablet of Hopton-Wood stone in the Children's Hospital, Brighton, for the LOUISE SASSOON ELECTRICAL & X RAY DEPARTMENT.

R 14 × 31; 1913.

275 Ledgerstone at Howden, nr Selby, Yorks., in memory of ROBERT STANLEY
SCHOLFIELD – 1841–1913.

> Simple and restrained.
> R 20 × 29; 1913.

276 Stone tablet on the Gyde Almshouses, Painswick, Glos., inscribed: THESE
ALMS HOUSES WERE BUILT AND ENDOWED BY EDWIN FRANCIS GYDE 1913.

> 1913.

277 Tablet of white marble, with green marble border, in memory of JAMES
FRANCIS HATFIELD-HARTER, d.1910.

> R 11 × 10; 1913.

278 Hopton-Wood stone tablet on the north wall of the chancel, Jesus College
Chapel, Cambridge, in memory of HENRY ARTHUR MORGAN, D.D., who served
the College for sixty-three years as Student, Fellow, Tutor and Master, d.1912.

> Nice ascenders from the 'A' and 'M'. 1913. (See also 562A)

278A Incised letters for Cambridge University REGIUS PROFESSOR OF PHYSIC
(within a lozenge) and LIBRARY.

> R 13 × 24; 1915.

279 Stone tablet at Royal Alexandra Children's Hospital, Brighton, 'These Open-Air
wards were erected & endowed in 1913 by Samuel Bythesea, late H.M. 51st Regt.,
Knight of S. John of Jerusalem …'

> Fine caps and spacious arrangement in the centre for the date, unusually large.
> R 19 × 35; 1913.

280 Portland headstone in the churchyard of St Giles', Packwood, Hockley Heath,
Warwick, in memory of LUCY JANE COUCHMAN, d.1913.

> An arch-headed stone with a generous moulding round the main inscription – which is
> centred, except the name. Below on the base is a seven-line Latin text in small caps
> spanning across the stone – CARITAS NUNQUAM EXCIDIT … FIDES, SPES, CARITAS:
> TRIA HAEC … CARITAS. 1914.

281 Tablet of white Sicilian marble commemorating the silver wedding of
HERBERT WILLIAM CRIBB and ALICE MARY CRIBB, 1888–1913, the parents of
Joseph and Laurie Cribb, E.G.'s assistants for many years.

> This bears overlapping hearts between the dates.
> R 10 × 12; c.1913.

282 Tablet in the North transept of Lincoln Cathedral in memory of WILLIAM
O'NEILL, M.D., C.M., M.R.C.P., London, 1830–1905.

> A long inscription mostly in lower case, the upper part nicely asymmetrical to allow for a
> shield and crest (no helm) and a well-designed motto ribbon.
> R 23 × 25; 1913.

> (See Weaver's *Memorials and Monuments*, 1915 – in which it is attributed to Macdonald Gill.)

283 Tablet with inscription, cut for an exhibition, in English and Latin: I AM THE FLOWER OF THE FIELD AND THE LILY OF THE VALLEYS. and: EGO FLOS CAMPI ET …

> The Latin is in rather naive 2¼ in. caps, the English in small caps (with one mistake, honestly corrected by inserting 'inter' above line 3).
>
> R 30 × 20; 1913.

*284 The fourteen Stations of the Cross, carved in low relief on Hopton-Wood stone, in Westminster Cathedral, London. The titles are in English, the texts in Latin.

> Designed by 1 April 1914; installed by June 1915; finished 11 March 1918. Details of mouldings, etc., of individual panels, and other drawings are dated 24 April 1914, signed either Eric Gill or E.G. The drawings are now in the Victoria & Albert Museum. The original small drawing for approval, about 10 in. square is in the British Museum.
> 68 × 68; 1914–18.
>
> Let into the floor, beneath the fourteenth Station, is a tablet cut by Laurie Cribb:
> E.G.LAPIDARIUS 1882–1940.

An appreciation of the inscriptions in each Station follows: I–XIV. All the titles are in large caps.

I 'Jesus is condemned to death'

> On the side of Pilate's seat, partly covered by his toga is 'Senatus populusque Romanus'. Behind his head, within the first of three arches is carved 'Quis est veritas?' The long inscription within the arches and divided boldly by the rounded columns reads 'Respondens universus populus dixit …' ('His blood be upon us …' etc.) And finishing '… ut cruc / ifi / ge / retur'. The lettering forms a substantial texture between Pilate, his kneeling servant and Jesus standing with his hands bound.
> (In St Cuthbert's, Bradford (see 386), the first Station, more economical in treatment than here, also has arches – and Pilate giving the 'thumbs down'.)

II 'Jesus receives his cross'

III 'Jesus falls the first time'

IV 'Jesus meets his mother'

> Above the kneeling figure of Mary is carved 'Benedicta tu in mulieribus' – the last two words interrupted by Jesus's fingers in blessing.

V 'Simon of Cyrene helps Jesus to carry the cross'

> This is on two lines with some unexpectedly large spaces between words.

VI 'Jesus and Veronica'

VII 'Jesus falls a second time'

VIII 'Jesus comforts the women of Jerusalem'

> The last four words are in small caps on two lines. An inscription of nineteen lines 'Jesus dixit O filiae Jerusalem nolite …' divides Jesus from the women. The texture is boldly interrupted by the cross.

IX 'Jesus falls a third time'

> A five-line inscription, divided by the cross and a soldier's helmet, reads 'Ne lecteris / inimica mea / super me quia cecidi consurgam cum sedero in tenebris dominus lux mea est'.

79

33 *Westminster Cathedral Stations of the Cross, the first Station: lettering as texture linking the figures, 1914–18 (284).*

I. JESUS IS CONDEMNED TO DEATH

34 *Westminster Cathedral Stations of the Cross, the fourteenth Station: lettering as a framing element, 1914–18, (284).*

XIV THE BODY OF JESUS IS LAID IN THE TOMB

X 'Jesus is stripped of his clothes'

The three-line text boldly spans the panel divided into four sections by the figures – 'Diviserunt sibi vestimenta mea …'

XI 'Jesus is nailed to the cross'

Across the top is 'Videbunt in quem transfixerunt'.

XII 'Jesus dies upon the cross'

Inscriptions in small caps are used here to contrast the big spaces of plain surface – 'Jesus dixit / consum / matum est' and at the foot 'Et vidimus eum et / non erat aspectus / vere languores / et desideravimus eum / nostros ipse tulit'. On the head of the cross, INRI in italic.

XIII 'The body of Jesus is taken from the cross and laid in Mary's bosom'

In two lines; INRI on the cross.

XIV 'The body of Jesus is laid in the tomb'

The title unnecessarily contains a joined HE. Across the beam over the tomb is 'Venit hora ut clarificetur filius hominis' (with UR joined as one). Down the side are sixteen short lines of caps – 'Amen, Amen dico vobis granum frumenti cadens …' ('Unless a grain of wheat falls …') On the side of the tomb five lines – 'Qui amat animam suam perdet eam …'.

284A Stone tablet, for an exhibition, OUR FATHER WHO ART IN HEAVEN … The Lord's Prayer; in caps in Latin, interlined in lower case in English.

R 14 × 35; 1914.

285 Inscription: MARY COOKE. 1839–1913.

R 4 × 14; 1914.

286A KING'S COLLEGE FOR WOMEN, Campden Hill, London, w.8, Architect, Charles Holden. Foundation Stone of Hopton-Wood stone, for Queen Mary's Hostel, laid by H.R.H. Princess Christian, 11 June 1914.

Very interesting italic caps in the heading with flourished Q.M.H. and a long 'L' in 'Hostel'.

286B Later, on a string course, 'the Marquess of Anglesey's Laboratories 1915' over a length of 78 ft.

286C Nine templates for 12 in. caps for the laboratories.

*287 Red granite cross at Upton-on-Severn, Worcs., in memory of GEORGE EDWARD MARTIN, 1829–1905, and MARIA HENRIETTA his wife, 1839–1912.

A short Celtic cross, the base of three steps with 2 in. raised letters well-fitted into all sides, excellently treated in very bold caps with a proper affinity with the granite: many small letters for spacing's sake. 'Blessed are the peace makers …' 1914. (See also 87A)

288 Inscription on Hopton-Wood stone for lamp and niche 18 in. high: LUMEN AD REVELATIONEM GENTIUM.

1914.

288A Incised lettering on an oak board, THE DECOY for the lintel of Joseph Thorp's 'Decoy Press' at Poling, Sussex.

> 1914.

289 Portland headstone formerly in Bisham churchyard, Berks., in memory of MALCOLM CORRIE POWELL, 1863–1913.

> The back bevelled and 'pillowed'. Understood to have been destroyed in an air raid, 1940. 1914.

290 Tall pillar sundial at Newnham College, Cambridge: 'In proud and grateful remembrance of the principalship of ELEANOR MILDRED SIDGWICK, 1892–1911, the Eastern Approach was widened and this Western Garden made 1914.'

> The panel follows the curve of the base within a moulded frame.
> 17 × 17; 1914. (See also 60)

291 Brass plate commemorating the gift of windows by Mary Ellen Creighton in memory of JANE CREIGHTON.

> 4 × 14; 1914. (See also 191)

292 Inscription of about seventy letters in roman caps on Hornton stone in memory of OWEN LITTLE, 1914.

293 Tablet of Hopton-Wood stone in memory of WINIFRED MARION SLATER – 1876–1914, Headmistress, September 1907 to March 1914.

> R 18 × 35; 1914.

294 Lettering: GUNNERY and NAVIGATION cut on the bases of two statues on the west side of the Admiralty Arch. Architect, Sir Aston Webb.

> This item was incorrectly listed in the Inventory as 'in the new arch, Buckingham Palace'.

295 Portland headstone in Bell's Hill Cemetery, Barnet, in memory of JOSEPH FRANK PAYNE – 1840–1910.

> Fine leaves in a generous space above the wide panel. An additional inscription was cut in 1932.
> R 13 × 22; 1914.

296 White marble tablet for Mortuary Chapel at Richmond, Surrey, erected by Constance and William Sandover in memory of their mothers, SUSANNAH ATHERTON of Richmond and MARY SANDOVER of Adelaide, Australia. 1914.

> R 17 × 52; 1914.

297 Tablet of Hopton-Wood stone in memory of ALEXANDER NIGEL TROTTER, Lieut. 3rd Battn. The Royal Scots, 1894–1914, at St Agatha's, Coates, Fittleworth, Sussex. 'Fighting in France for his King and Country.'

> R 11 × 30; 1915.

298 Headstone and kerbing of Portland stone at Hampstead in memory of … CALDERON.

> 1914.

299 Two-line inscription on base of statue: THE BURGHERS OF CALAIS / AUGUSTE RODIN in Victoria Tower Gardens, Westminster, London, S.W.1.

> 60 × 8; 1914.

300 Inscription on panel for Norman & Burt, Stonemasons, Burgess Hill: WEIGHT SHOULD NOT BE PLACED UPON THE CONCRETE CEILINGS.

> R 5 × 14; 1914.

301 Bronze tablet fixed to an oak cross at St Mary's, Headingley, Surrey, in memory of HERBERT EDGAR REID of 'The Oaks', Walton Heath, d.1914.

> The arched top contains an engaging IN; the rest is a good unselfconscious statement. The earliest drawing says the lettering to be modelled in wax or gesso and cast in bronze. E.G.'s full-size setting-out of the inscription adds 'for E.W.Gimson'. Perhaps this explains the simple detail of the oak.
> 19 × 7; 1914.

302 Hopton-Wood stone tablet in Manchester University: 'To the memory of GEORGE ROBERT GISSING, 1857–1903, student of Owens College, 1872–1876.' Novelist.

> Simple caps within a surround of banded pilasters and a bold cornice. Illustrated in Weaver's Memorials and Monuments, 1915.
> R 10 × 23; 1914.

303 Inscription commemorating the restoration and enlargement of the church room, St Mary the Virgin, Primrose Hill, London, in memory of the Revd A.SPENCER, 'that devoted priest who passed away on Innocents' Day 1913, whose soul may God prosper in the light'.

> The last line is in italic with an unusual capital 'R'.
> R 23 × 36; c.1914.

304 Tablet for the grave of a dog (Wang): INSTAR AMORIS ERAT NVNC AVREVS INTER AMORES ACCIPITVR CAESPES PRAETEGIT OSSA CANIS. MCMXIV. Reported to be at Lawford Hall, Manningtree, Essex.

> R 4 × 13; c.1914.

305 Inscriptions: OPERA MANUUM NOSTRARUM DIRIGE SUPER NOS: ET OPUS MANUUM NOSTRARUM DIRIGE.

> Probably two practice pieces; a capital 'R' in the lower case.
> R 9 × 18; 1915.

306 Inscription at 21 Filey Road, Scarborough recording damage by German shell-fire in 1914 and the building's restoration in 1915: HOC AEDIFICIUM ANNO DOMINI MDCCCCXIV TORMENTIS HOSTIUM VERBERATUM GERMANORUM PROXIMO ANNO RESTAURATUM BARBARIAM TESTATUR.

> R 17 × 53; 1915.

307 Inscription in memory of MARY HAMILTON widow of John Hamilton of Brownshall & St Ernans Island, Co.Donegal.

A capital 'R' in the italic.
R 16 × 24; 1915. (See 322)

308 Carving of font, St Joseph's (R.C.) Church, Pickering, Yorks.

An item included in the Inventory but without an inscription. 1916.

309 In Lincoln Cathedral, an inscription of 191 2 in. incised letters and thirty-five raised and gilded letters on the pedestal of a bronze seated statue of EDWARD KING – 1829–1910, Bishop of Lincoln 1885–1910. Sculptor, Sir William Richmond.

The small 'V'-cut lettering of the sides (St Matthew 5.5–8 and St John 4.7) is hard to see, due to the purply, strongly grained marble. The fine raised letters on the front are better, and the feeling for scale and response to the site are in character. 1915.

310 Roll of Honour on oak tablet, commemorating those members of the staff of John Eede Butt & Sons, Littlehampton, who gave their lives 1914–1918.

Three lines of caps; then the names, but justified to the left.
R 30 × 21; c.1919.

311 Base of cross of Hopton-Wood stone, St Mary, Bayford, Hertford, in memory of HARRIET C. HORNBY, 1840–1915.

The cross tapers from 6 in. at the foot to 5 in., and narrower at the ends of the arms. The foot is nicely gathered above the base with large curved bevels. The base, about 2 ft square, is weathered in all directions. Simple caps on the base: 'Nothing in my hand I bring …'
R 13 × 25; 1915.

On the back of the base is a memorial to Revd CHARLES EDWARD HORNBY, d.1918.
(See 343A/P)

*312 Mural tablet in St Mary and St Nicholas, Trumpington, Cambridge, in memory of FRANCIS PERCY CAMPBELL PEMBERTON, Captain 2nd Life Guards, killed in action 1914, aged 29.

A very distinguished work, within narrow pilasters and mouldings. Sixteen lines largely in lower case, and italic at the foot. Unusually, the words are centred, giving much emphasis to 'only son' on a single line. The tablet 'is placed here by a few of his friends in token of their sorrow & in perpetual remembrance of his example'.

(Gill proposed his familiar capital 'R's in the italic lower case, but these were evidently not approved.)
R 29 × 19; 1915.

312A/P A stone garden roller, one end carved with leaves and raised caps: DITCHLING COMMON 1915, the other with a floral interlacing design with lobes and six leaves round a simple four-leaf clover.

The floral end is in high relief, the other is much weathered. The caps are informal, with pointed tops to the 'M's. (The iron handle is not, as usually, at 90° to the shaft, but angled so as to be easier to pull.)
22½ diam. × 20; 1915.

313 Headstone of Hopton-Wood stone (stated in the Inventory to be at Broughty Ferry, Dundee, Tayside, in memory of JOHN EDMOND GORDON – 1864–1914.
1915.

*314 Hopton-Wood stone tablet, surmounted by a coat of arms, in St Mary the Virgin, Stratfieldsaye, Berks., in memory of 'The Lord RICHARD WELLESLEY, Captain, of No 3 Compy 1st Battn Grenadier Guards, 2nd son of Arthur, 4th Duke of Wellington, born 30 Sept 1879, killed 29 Oct 1914 at Ypres, Belgium fighting in the Great War against the Germans.'

> Blue caps, finely disposed and centred: e.g. in line three, to fit the line, COMPY with the 'M' and 'P' combined and the 'Y' very small. At the foot, a cross, and below this 'His wife Nesta set this stone here in his memory', in similar caps but five letters with extended ascenders and descenders. The arms above – coloured and gilt but not differenced, with an esquire's helm and spiky mantling – have a good curved motto ribbon, and the motto in blue caps, 'Virtutis for / tuna comes', boldly divided by the shield. All below the shield is flanked by shallow pilasters. Beneath the tablet is a narrow base cut with three fleurs-de-lys and 'W.W.' in relief and gilded. The siting was changed from the east wall of the transept to the west to allow the crest to face towards the altar.
>
> R 36 × 20; 1917. (See Plate VIII in the Inventory for the first design, IX for the rubbing.)

315 Tablet of Hopton-Wood stone with letters coloured in red and blue on north wall of Broxwood R.C. Church, Leominster, Herefordshire, in memory of Lieut. RICHARD MARY SNEAD-COX, Royal Scots, 'killed in action near Neuve Chapelle 28th October, 1914, aged 21, and Lieut. GEOFFREY PHILIP JOSEPH SNEAD-COX, Royal Welch Fusiliers, killed in action near Ypres 21st October, 1914, aged 19: eldest sons of the Lord of the Manor of Broxwood.'

> Within a camber arch are crossed swords, dividing 'In memory' and 'of'. Asymmetrically placed caps for the principal names. Roman lower case sometimes but mainly a free italic with cap 'R's: then unexpectedly – and rarely – small caps for the last line, 'Greater love than this hath no man'. A very fine and characteristic work.
>
> R 36 × 29; 1915.

316 A pent-roofed cross of Portland stone in Wimbledon Cemetery in memory of HENRY CRAUFORD BARNARD, 1861–1915.

> This has the memorial panel part way up the tapered cross shaft; a bold and unusual work. 1915.

316A/P Headstone at Weybridge churchyard of MARY ALICE CLUTTON-BROCK d.1915.

> With a pair of doves above in low relief; eleven lines mostly in lower case. 'O all ye fowls of the air Bless ye the Lord ...' and 'Our soul is escaped even as a bird out of the snare of the fowler: the snare is broken and we are delivered' – the lettering has an overall texture. 1915. (See 482)

317 Hopton-Wood stone tablet with semi-circular top commemorating the building of a hospital in 1915 by Ellen Odette Ulick O'Connor, wife of William, 4th Earl of Desart, in memory of OTWAY FREDERICK SEYMOUR CUFFE, 3rd son of Otway O'Connor, 3rd Earl of Desart.

> Normal upper and lower case. 1916.

318 Portland headstone with elegantly shaped top in churchyard of St Mary the Virgin, Painswick, Glos., in memory of MARY CATHERINE GERE – 1842–1916.

> R 21 × 10; 1916.

319 Lettering on doors, etc., for the offices of the Crown Agents for the Colonies, Millbank, London.

1916.

(In his diary for 1916 E.G. recorded several entries regarding lettering for this building, on various dates March – May 23.)

320 Inscription on front of the alabaster altar in the Chapel of the Incarnation, St Osmund's, Parkstone, Dorset: CARO MEA VERE EST CIBUS SANGUIS MEUS VERE EST POTUS.

The lettering, on a low-relief roundel, is boldly divided by the arms of a cross which extends to the edges of the circle. Architect, E.S. Prior, with Arthur Grove. 1916.

320A/P SACRISTY at St Osmund's, Parkstone, and a cross in relief over the keystone.

Bold raised caps within a recessed panel on a lintel. 1916.

320B/P St Osmund's, Parkstone: All Souls Altar, as war memorial.

Gilded caps on blue background on the retable – VICIT LEO DE TRIBU JUDA; and below, on the face of the altar, three panels each with one word, ORA / PRO / NOBIS – the 'nobis' being in smaller caps, to fit the panel. 1916.

320C/P St Osmund's, Parkstone: Lady Altar, raised lettering on the reredos in gilded caps, '+ ECCE ANCILLA DOMINI +' and a text along the lower border in memory of CAROLINE LOUISA RENDELL.

The letters form lively bands within a richly decorated scheme (by Macdonald Gill?). 1916.

321 Brass plate in memory of PHILIP BERNARD WINGATE, Rector of Tarrant Keynston, Dorset, 1904–1913, and of his aunt. (Not in Winchester Cathedral, as stated in the Inventory.)

A simple centred inscription of caps and lower case, engraved by George Friend. R 26 × 16; 1916.

322 Inscription of 550 1½ in. caps on a panel of Grey Roman stone opposite the jetty on a causeway between the island of St Ernans and the mainland of Co. Donegal, Ireland, in memory of JOHN HAMILTON, J.P., D.L., of Brownshall and St Ernans, 1800–1884.

The composition of the text in E.G.'s drawing is one of his finest. Justified to the left, and with two lines significantly short, the size seems to have been determined by the length of the penultimate line. 'This causeway stands to commemorate the great mutual love between John Hamilton and the people of Donegal both his own tenants and others. Through a lifetime of bitter hunger and pestilence John Hamilton, not for the first time, stood between them and death. Knowing that his great wish was to build a road joining the island of St Ernans, his favourite dwelling place, with the mainland, that owing to the Atlantic tides he could not achieve this without expenditure far beyond his means, the people, Roman Catholic and Protestant, came in their hundreds with spade pick and barrow and built this causeway refusing all recompence. John Hamilton; JP; DL; of Brownshall and St Ernans was born in the year 1800. He succeeded his father in 1807 and died in 1884.'
Full-size setting out. 19 × 68; 1916. (See also 307)

322A Tablet inscribed: AGNUS DEI QUI TOLLIS PECCATA MUNDI DONA NOBIS
PACEM.

> R 8 × 18; 1916.

323 Portland headstone in Willesden Jewish Cemetery, Beaconsfield Rd, London
N.W.10, in memory of ALPHONSE COURLANDER, d.1914.

> With pilasters, and the top cambered: simple caps and lower case, now weathered away.
> R 10 × 16; 1916.

324 Recumbent gravestone of Forest of Dean stone at Hagley, Worcs. – in memory
of ALFRED LYTTELTON, 1857–1913. The text, below a simple shield, crest and
motto, runs: 'Here is laid the body Born February 7 1857 Died July 5 1913 of
ALFRED LYTTELTON. The radiance of his being drew all men to him. He gave
freely of his treasure and he was deeply loved.' Finally in caps, 'He hath anointed
thee with the oil of gladness above thy fellows.' A cross device below in low
relief.

> The layout of the twelve lines of text is distinguished and spacious.
> 77 × 28; 1917.

> (An earlier version described the deceased as 'athlete, lawyer, statesman' and 'He was
> what every man would wish his son to be, pure and joyous, chivalrous and just – a very
> brave and gracious soul.')

325 Hopton-Wood stone tablet (said to be in a church near Malvern) in memory of
EVERARD FERGUSON CALTHROP, 1876–1915, with coat of arms.

> The shield bears three caltraps (a pun on the name) – a spiked hazard designed to lame
> horses, a 'cheval trap', in fact. And the inscription: O TU FELIX. 1917.

326 Inscription on stone: DOMINE JESU CHRISTE QUI DIXISTI PETITE ET
DABITUR VOBIS: DA MIHI GRATIAM UT ROGEM QUOD TIBI PLACEAT QUI
VIVIS ET REGNAS DEUS PER OMNIA SAECULA SAECULORUM. AMEN.

> Eight lines of which nos 1 and 2 are full length, 3 justified to the left, 4–6 full width, 7 in
> smaller caps to fit; and 8 (Amen) centred and widely spaced. Thus is interest gained in an
> otherwise simple text.
> R 17 × 21; 1916.

327 Tablet of Hopton-Wood stone, letters black and red, in memory of
Capt. ANDREW DONALD HUTTON. (Said to be in a Glasgow church.)

> Caps and lower case, centred.
> R 29 × 22; 1917.

328 Tablet of Hopton-Wood stone letters, coloured black and red, in memory of
Capt. JOHN MACDONALD, Highland Light Infantry, killed in action at Gallipoli
13 July 1915. (Said to be in a church in or near Glasgow.)

> R 11 × 20; 1917.

329 Brass tablet, inlaid in an ebony panel, with engraved letters coloured black and
red, in memory of CHARLES CHETWODE BAILY, d.1914. (Understood to have
been in the Royal Alexandra Hospital for Sick Children, Brighton.)

Fine caps and lower case, engraved by George Friend.
R 22 × 21; 1916.

330 Tablet with a fourteen-line inscription of a poem by Frances Cornford, 'In
Dorset': FROM MUDDY ROAD TO MUDDY LANE I PLODDED THROUGH THE
FALLING RAIN ...

A grand work but poor letters, assumed to be cut by a pupil. The poem appeared in the
collection of Frances Cornford's poems *Spring Morning*, Poetry Bookshop, 1915.
R 24 × 35; c.1916.

331 Inscription: BAD WORKMEN QUARREL WITH THEIR TOOLS BECAUSE
GOOD WORKMEN DO NOT USE BAD TOOLS, now in the Ditchling Museum.

Assumed to be cut by a pupil: two sprays of leaves at the foot. Red and blue caps.
11 × 13; c.1916.

331A Pen and ink drawing of an alphabet for 1½ in. wood letters in roman capitals.

The drawing of this alphabet is signed: 'Wood engraved alphabet. E.G. 1916 circa.'

332 Brass plate: THE CENTRAL LIBRARY FOR STUDENTS (London).

This library was founded by Dr Albert Mansbridge, largely with a view to supplying books
to the University Tutorial and Workers Education Association. The original library
premises are now part of the University of London.
R 9 × 7; 1916.

333 Tablet in white metal in memory of HUGH ARNOLD, Lieutenant, 8th Battn.
Northumberland Fusiliers. Killed in action at Suvla Bay, August 1916, aged 43.
QUS FATA VACATUS.

8 × 18; 1917.

334 Portland headstone, St Andrew's, Burgess Hill, Sussex, the inscription
surmounted by a crucifix, in memory of JOHN EDWIN NYE, 1885–1916, who
died of wounds received in the Great War.

A curved and moulded top, and pilasters. 1917.

335 Tablet of Hopton-Wood stone in memory of IAN SAWERS SCOTT, 2nd Lieut.,
2nd Battn King's Own Scottish Borderers, killed in action on the Somme, 1 July
1916.

Simple caps and lower case.
R 12 × 19; 1917.

336 Inscription of two lines of caps, PASTOR EST TUI DOMINUS, below a bas-relief
carving of the head of Christ.

Formerly built into the fabric above the entrance to Hopkins Crank where E.G. lived on
Ditchling Common. PASTOR widely spaced and with the leg of the 'R' swung out. A very
distinguished work, now in the Samuels Collection, University of Texas at Austin. The
rubbing is endorsed 'made for D.P[epler].'
R 3 × 14; 1917.

*337 Wayside crucifix with pent roof at Bisham, Berks. In memory of FREDERICK SEPTIMUS KELLY D.S.C. 'Remember likewise his comrades in arms of this countryside':

> Here follow eleven names with contractions where needed to get the texture right. On the north, details of Lieut. Kelly's naval actions; on the front: JESU MY STRENGTH AND MY REDEEMER; and on the base: HERE WAS A ROYAL FELLOWSHIP OF DEATH. The shaft tapers up, above inverted half circles where the base is gathered in. 1917. (See also 344)

338 Inscription in Latin incised direct on the south wall of the interior of the tower, St Andrew's, Mells, Somerset, in memory of RAYMOND ASQUITH – 1878–1916, surmounted by a bronze wreath designed by Lutyens. Raymond Asquith was married to Katharine Horner of Mells Park.

> The eleven lines of small caps, centred, are in red, and therefore not very clear in the rough surface of the stone. Below are the dates defined in blue; being in roman numerals they form a fine extended base. Blue also for the small cross at the start of the words in red. 1917. (See also 414; and at Mells, three associated designs by Lutyens 175, 175A/P and 176.)

338A/P Hopton-Wood stone tablet: 'Pray for the soul of BERNARD MORGAN who gave his life at sea Oct 9th 1917 Aged 18. R.I.P.'

> Six lines, massed, the last three justified to left. Formerly in the chapel at Ditchling. 9 × 9; 1917.

339 Hopton-Wood stone tablet on the north wall of the chancel of St Mary's, Walberton, Arundel, in memory of PHILIP BLAKEWAY, Vicar of Walberton 1907–1915, Chaplain to the London Mounted Brigade who died on active service at Ismailia, June 16, 1915: MORI LUCRUM.

> Below a rounded top and a gilded cross, the inscription has an informality of lower case, italic and caps, in red and black. 20 × 12; 1917.

340 Tablet of Portland stone with an eight-line inscription in Latin and English: TU ES PETRUS SUPER HANC PETRAM …

> Lines 1, 2, 4, 6 and 8 are in caps in Latin, lines 3, 5 and 7 in English, lower case; beautifully contrasted, and justified to the left. It was cut for exhibition purposes, and shown at the Alpine Club Gallery in May 1918. It is now built into a wall at Pigotts, High Wycombe, though sadly cracked. Carefully dimensioned to suit eight courses of brick. 24 × 19; 1918.

*340A An eight-line inscription in red roman caps, cut direct in the wall below a window in All Saints, Thorney Hill, Bransgore, Christchurch, Hants – built as a private chapel of the Manners family, architect, Detmar Blow – in memory of JOHN MANNERS, killed in action 1914. The text written by the Hon. John Fortescue, runs: 'To the beloved memory of a Lieutenant in His Majesty's Grenadier Guards who fell in victorious combat with the German infantry among the woodlands of Villers Cotterets in the north of France and lies in one grave with an hundred British soldiers, his comrades of a devoted rearguard. At peace in the silence of the forest.'

The lines of fine caps are progressively smaller to the foot, where the last line is affected by the angels carved in high relief at the sides. In front of the inscription is a bronze effigy by Sir Bertram McKennal (1917) on a tomb chest with three shields in panels. Altogether a very distinguished work.

24 × 44; 1918. (See also 97 and 389)

341 An exhibition piece, in roman caps – IT LASTETH AND FOREVER SHALL FOR GOD LOVETH IT.

R 6 × 17; 1918.

342 Stone carving of a pietà after a design by the Revd Desmond Chute, bearing an inscription in Old French worded: MVLT AD APRIS KI BIEN CONUIST AHAN. ('He has learnt much who has known [much] suffering well'. From *The Song of Roland*, line 2524, tirade 184.)

The last word is composed of two pairs of conjoined letters.
R 13 × 18; 1918.

343 Hopton-Wood stone tablet, St Eadburgha, Ebrington, Chipping Campden, Glos., in memory of EDWARD HORNBY, 1833–1918.

Raised letters within recessed lines of mixed heights; not characteristic lettering, but drawn out by E.G. 1918. (See also 311 for his grave.)

343A/P Inscription on the base of the cross of Harriet Hornby (311) in memory of Revd CHARLES EDWARD HORNBY former Vicar of Ebrington d.1918.

'After he had served his generation, by the Will of God he fell asleep', in italic in E.G.'s usual way at the foot. c.1918.

344 Brass plate, with inscription in Latin in the antechapel at Eton College in memory of Lieut. FREDERICK SEPTIMUS KELLY, d.1916.

Nineteen lines, mostly in rather crowded lower case, the name in red and caps. Above AMDG, and a crest of a bird and anchor over a motto, STEADY, and HOOD BATTN. A very distinguished work, set among a very mixed company of memorial plaques.
R 14 × 8; 1918. (See also 337)

345 A sort of three-layer ledgerstone in the churchyard of St Margaret's, Ditchling, in memory of WILLIAM WAKEFORD ATTREE, d.1862, and of THOMAS ATTREE, d.1863.

The ridge has a raised cross over almost the full length; long inscriptions in two sizes of caps. Thomas Attree died 1863 'in the 86th year of his age, having survived W.W. Attree his only son 1 year & 11 days. "It is the Lord let him do what seemeth him good".'
9 × 40 and 8 × 47; 1918.

346 Incised inscription in Ditchling churchyard in memory of Corporal WALTER HARVEY, d.1917.

The inscriptions are on kerbs round a normal War Graves Commission headstone. Cpl Harvey died of wounds received in action 1917 aged 25; one kerb also commemorates Private Alec Harvey, killed in action 1918 aged 25.
c.48 and 24 × 4; 1918.

*347 Village cross as war memorial of Portland and Purbeck stone at Affpuddle, Bere Regis, Dorset.

> An austere sculptured memorial of great authority, 25 ft high, beautifully sited at a road junction. The shaft bears on one side, below a small aedicule, a figure of Christ with a great sword, on the other, the Madonna and Child below a bold projecting roof, carved with the Agnus Dei, supported on Purbeck shafts. Set on four steps the base has recessed arches bearing just five names. Round the base above the arches is carved (from Julian of Norwich) 'It is sooth that sin was cause of all this pain; and all shall be well ...' 1916–18.
>
> The lettering was re-cut by Donald Potter about 1970, after becoming weathered. Further names (1939–45) added c.1993.

348 Inscription on stone: OPTIMA ET PVLCHERRIMA VITAE SVPELLEX AMICITIA.

> R 4 × 27; 1918.

349 Stone tablet, in memory of MARY ANNE WALLIS, d.1918.

> R 16 × 26; 1919.

350 Inscription in Greek on a holy water stoup, commissioned by Frank Rinder: ΠΗΓΗ ΥΔΑΤΟΣ ('Christ the spring of water').

> R 3 × 5; 1918.

351 Inscription for a figure of Christ in Hopton-Wood stone, painted in black, blue and red: IESU, IESU, IESU ESTO MIHI IESUS.

> Done in collaboration with Desmond Chute; Eric Gill's last carving prior to joining the forces, 12 September 1918.
> R 22 × 26; 1918.

352 QUID SIBI VOLUNT ISTI? / ET SI AD TE PERTINENT? / RESPONDIT: PARVULI QUOS / DONAVIT MIHI DEUS SERVO TUO. Bought for the Samuels collection, now at the University of Texas at Austin.

> It seems likely that the inscription was the work of a pupil. In his diary for 26 July 1924, E.G. recorded: 'Re-cutting inscription "Quid sibi ..." (for R. A. Walker) all day'.
> R 11 × 39; c.1918.

353 Gravestone, with kerbing of Portland stone, in memory of JANE, wife of ROBERT WHITEHEAD, d.1918 and of their son RONALD, d.1918.

> R 36 × 11; 1919.

354 Marble tablet in Rugby School Chapel, with bas-relief portrait by Havard Thomas, in memory of RUPERT BROOKE – 1887–1915, followed by his sonnet, 'The Soldier'.

> Unusually the verse is in half-inch caps massed. Line eleven is too long for the width of the panel, so the last word – 'given' – is embraced by an upward stroke from the 'D' of DAY in the next line.
> R 14 × 19; 1919.

355 Narrow ledgerstone, St Mary's, Storrington, Sussex, in memory of ARTHUR FRANCIS BELL, d.1918.

This is divided across the centre with 'Lux perpetua luceat ei.' A very simple and distinguished stone. 1919.

*356 War memorial cross of Portland stone in the churchyard of St Mary, Harting, Sussex. 1919. With sculptured panels of St George, St Richard and the draught of fishes.

The names are in arches on the base formed of a flattish rounded moulding. E.G. makes it clear on the drawing, 'This is not a true circle'.
22 ft high; 1920.

357 Gravestone with cross in the churchyard of St John the Baptist, Wivelsfield, Sussex, in memory of RICHARD TYRELL GODMAN – 1911–1918.

The cross has a pent roof. E.G.'s drawing notes a tapering of the cross from 5 in. square at the foot to 4½ in. at the crossbar. 1919.

358 Hopton-Wood stone tablet in the cloisters of the Priory of Our Lady of Good Counsel, Haywards Heath, Sussex. The Latin inscription records the granting of an indulgence by the Bishop of Southwark.

Six lines in lower case.
14 × 14; 1919.

358A/P Tablet with a shield surmounted by a coronet, in memory of VICTOR, 5th MARQUESS CONYNGHAM, d.1918. Location unknown.

1919.

*359 War memorial of Portland stone at Chirk, near Oswestry.

This great monument, about 15 ft high and 3 ft square, has a form of pediment on all sides. At the base is a stone seat. On the south face is a bas-relief of a soldier 'on watch' with right hand holding a rifle and left hand upraised; tin-hatted and great-coated. Below this is a nine-line inscription in large caps. 'To the memory of those habitants and indwellers of the parish of Chirk who gave up their lives for the cause of their country [This line being longer, there are two joined examples of HE, and a small OF] during the war of 1914–1919. This monument was established by their fellows of the Parish.' Below this in 4 in. caps begins the text which runs round three sides of the base, 'In righteousness / shall they / make war. Rev. XIX'. (The 'R' of WAR develops into a large flower, or leaved bud.) The seventy names are in columns justified to the left.

The work was commissioned by Lord Howard de Walden, at that time living at Chirk Castle. In a note to him E.G. wrote, 'Soldier on the look out – the most typical attitude representing the war of entrenchment'. 1920.

360 Tombstone in Wivelsfield Churchyard, Haywards Heath, Sussex, in memory of ANNIE TRUMBLE, d.1917.

R 12 × 8; 1919.

361 War memorial tablet of Hopton-Wood stone, St Mary the Virgin, Cloughton, Yorks., 1919.

The memorial has eleven names, coloured, within a bas-relief wreath, above which is cut in small caps, 'Their name liveth for evermore'. Vertically, beside the names are cut: PRO

and PATRIA, and below them R.I.P. The four spaces left at the corners outside the wreath are filled with large raised and gilt letters A.M.D.G..
41 × 48; 1919.

362 Portland headstone, surmounted by a crucifix in relief in Godalming New Cemetery, Surrey, in memory of CARL TRESSLER, 1851–1918.

The headstone, tapered slightly towards the base is shaped interestingly at the top to form a cross. 1919.

363 War memorial pillar on a base surrounded by a stone seat at Ditchling, Sussex. The names of twenty men are incised on the south face. The words, 'Greater love hath no man than this, that a man lay down his life for his friends', are incised round the plinth.

1919.

364 War memorial tablet in Hopton-Wood stone, for the church of St George the Martyr, Ham, Kent.

In eleven lines the names are in caps, the regiments or ships in italic; coloured in red and black. E.G. gave a rough detail of the border in interlacing bands, 'or anything else you prefer!'
25 × 42; 1919.

*365 War memorial tablet of Hopton-Wood stone coloured black and red in entrance hall of the Victoria & Albert Museum.

This fine memorial, integrated between pilasters on bold corbels, is surmounted by a cambered arch containing a branch of laurel. The upper part of the inscription is centred and cleverly shaped, with the dates in roman numerals larger, forming a base for this part. The sixteen names follow, justified to the left. On the base of the frame, in italic, is a record of the subscriptions by the staff. The bold corbels bear a monogram of V & A and, unusually, the 'signatures' of J.C. (Joseph Cribb) and E.G. in tiny letters alongside.
58 × 26; 1920.

366 Headstone of Hopton-Wood stone in the Roman Catholic Cemetery, Kensal Green, in memory of VIOLET MARY HOLLAND – 1881–1918.

On a round-headed stone with a cross at the top, the memorial text in caps and lower case is followed, in italic, by a quotation adapted from Spenser's The Faerie Queene – 'Sleepe after toyle, love after torment, Ease after warre, Death after life Does greatly please.'
40 × 22; 1919.

367 Inscription on base of a cross in the churchyard of SS Peter and Paul, Hareby, Spilsby, Lincs. in memory of MARIAN HAIRBY WINGATE, 1826–1916.

The boldness of the base is echoed in that of the caps in the inscription. The shaft and arms of the simple Latin cross are tapered with great subtlety. On the reverse is alpha, omega, a chi-rho and a fish.
11 × 16; 1919.

368 Headstone in Hove Cemetery in memory of WILLIAM HERBERT BOND, 1862–1918, Headmaster of Brighton Municipal School of Art, 1905–1918.

The caps are enlivened by a cheerfully extended 'L'. A small and distinguished stone. It stands within earlier kerbing, not by E.G.

30 × 13; 1919.

369 Tablet for a house in memory of GERRARD CHOWNE, Artist, 1875–1917 – Captain, East Lancs. Regiment, killed in action at Salonica, 1917.

Five lines of caps and lower case, then four of italic.

20 × 25; 1919.

370 Stone tablet beneath a statue of St George on the north wall in the Clare Chapel, St Mary the Virgin, Rye, Sussex, in memory of Vice-Admiral Sir GEORGE WARRENDER, Bt, K.C.B., d.1917.

R 6 × 9; 1919.

371 Oak panel for the Cornfords' house at Conduit Head, Madingley Rd, Cambridge, now destroyed.

1920.

*372 Tablet of Portland stone in Winchester Cathedral, with a coat of arms, in memory of Brigadier-General JOHN EDMOND GOUGH, V.C., C.B., C.M.G., b.1871, died of wounds February 1915.

A twenty-two line inscription (sited immediately above No. 387 within a laurel wreath) is well integrated into the panelling of the medieval wall. The original drawings show that much care was given to the coat of arms. In the event the shield is 'canted', together with the crest 'to the sinister', thus towards the altar, as is proper. The mantling is of E.G.'s spiky sort, and forms a vigorous silhouette within the cusps of the arch. The motto ribbon is partly hidden behind the base of the shield, dividing the word 'Diverso' into two – but enlivening the silhouette. (See Plate X in the *Inventory* for an earlier version.)

R 41 × 29; 1920.

373 Inscribed tablet, with bas-relief portrait head in St Michael's, Amberley, Sussex, in memory of JOAN MARY STRATTON, d.1919 aged 17 – 'Dear child'.

R 24 × 11; 1920.

374 War memorial tablet of Hopton-Wood stone in St Mary's, Betteshanger, Kent.

Caps, in black, for the names in full; lower case, in red, for regiments, etc. surrounded by a leafy border.

30 × 24; 1920.

375 Memorial tablet of Hopton-Wood stone formerly in St Luke's Church, West Holloway, London, N.7, in memory of Dr RICHARD GLOVER, the first vicar of the parish, 1869–1898. The tablet was destroyed when the church was badly damaged by enemy action during World War II.

376 Inscription on the plinth of the equestrian statue on Horse Guards Parade, London, of Field Marshal Viscount WOLSELEY, K.P., G.C.B., O.M., G.C.M.G. 1833–1913, 'Commander in Chief of the British Army 1895–1900'.

The statue was 'cast from machine guns taken in Lord Wolseley's campaigns …' and a list of nine of them follows, from 1852 to 1885. (Sculptor, Goscombe John.) 1920.

35 *War memorial at Chirk, Clwyd. Rubbing of one side of the base, 1920 (359).*

36 *War memorial, Victoria & Albert Museum, with monograms on the corbels, 1920 (365).*

377 War memorial tablet of Portland stone, in red and black, in St Peter and St Paul, West Wittering, Chichester, 1920 (where E.G.'s father, the Revd A. T. Gill, was Vicar). This contains the name of Capt. Kenneth Carlyle Gill M.C. killed in France 1918.

> This is an excellent example of E.G.'s originality of approach to design: below a hefty cornice, the pilasters are of very different heights, responding to the site; names in lower case justified to the left; strong lines for the dates; and an unusually sloping italic at the foot – 'Greater love hath no man ...' and a final line in caps.
> R 29 × 33; 1920.

378 Inscriptions on sides of a garden roller 18 in. diameter: COME ALL YOU FALSE YOUNG MEN DO NOT LEAVE ME HERE TO COMPLAIN and FOR THE GRASS THAT HAS OFTEN TIMES BEEN TRAMPLED UNDER FOOT GIVE IT TIME IT WILL RISE UP AGAIN.

> Inscribed for Ethel Mairet, the weaver, of Gospels, Ditchling, the roller is now in the Holburne Museum's Craft Study Centre, Bath. 1920.

379 Hopton-Wood stone tablet for Melbourne Museum, Australia, recording a gift by JOHN CONNELL in February 1914, commissioned by Mrs Frank Rinder, Cambridge.

> 12 × 15; 1920.

379A Inscription: OPERA MANUUM NOSTRARUM DIRIGE SUPER NOS ET OPUS MANUUM NOSTRARUM DIRIGE.

> Simple caps on a camber-arched stone.
> R 12 × 18; 1920.

379B Inscriptions; Latin and English in alternate lines, the Latin in roman capitals (black), the English lower case (red). HOMINES DIVITES IN VIRTUTE ... and 'Men rich in virtue studying beautifulness'.

> 1920.

380 War memorial cross at Angmering, Sussex, with inscription on base.

> Unusually, E.G.'s note on the drawing says, 'All lettering to be accurately centred'. This may well have been at the request of the parish, since E.G.'s normal practice, for economy of time in setting out, and for liveliness of an inscription, was to justify to the left. 1920.

381 War memorial pillar at Stanway, Glos., with a bronze St George and Dragon about 9-ft high by Alexander Fisher. On a panel on the base are carved the names. Two other panels read: MEN OF STANWAY / 1914–1918 / FOR A TOMB / THEY HAVE AN ALTAR / FOR LAMENTATION / MEMORY / AND FOR PITY / PRAISE, and FOR YOUR TO-MORROW WE GAVE OUR TO-DAY.

> For the stone base of the pillar, designed by Sir Philip Stott, the lowest three steps are cut in the shape of a Tudor rose. Below the top of the pillar, on a square stone, are cut 'France' and 'Egypt'. The memorial was commissioned by the Countess of Wemyss; her sons, Ego (Lord Elcho) and Yvo Charteris, died while serving in Egypt and France. 1920. (See 381A, 720, 733A and 756)

*381A War memorial in St Peter's, Stanway, Glos.

> The names are carved on the reveals of a window within shallow arches. This is one of the most successful examples of E.G.'s integration of lettering into an architectural setting, the transverse light clearly showing the 'V'-cut names. Commissioned by the Countess of Wemyss.
> c. 30 × 20; 1920. (See also 381, 720, 733A and 756)

382 Memorial cross and gravestone in the crypt of St Paul's Cathedral, in memory of Field-Marshal Earl ROBERTS, V.C., 1832–1914.

> The cross, of black polished stone, slightly tapered, is on the wall and bears the single name ROBERTS. The gravestone, a slab of York stone, is at the foot of the cross, inscribed: ROBERTS / INDIA / 1832 / FRANCE / 1914. (See Plate XI in the *Inventory*.) 1921.

383 Bronze tablet on the west wall of the ante-chapel at Eton College, the inscription surmounted by a coat of arms, in memory of Major Lord DESMOND FITZGERALD, M.C., 1888–1916, 1st Battn, Irish Guards, 2nd son of 5th Duke of Leinster and of HERMIONE his wife.

> A very distinguished work largely in lower case slightly condensed; seventeen lines. 1920. (See also 344, 485 nearby and 592)

384 Portland headstone in memory of MONICA SHOVE, 1883–1919, with a bas-relief and three figures.

> 1920.

385 Inscription in memory of ELIZABETH SILVESTER of the Slade School, London, d. 1920 aged 80 years.

> The stone contains widely spaced italic within a low pediment shape.
> R 7 × 42; 1920.

385A/P Ledgerstone at Belmont Abbey, Hereford in memory of F.X. Stewart, with a crucifix in high relief above the inscription.

> The sides of the ledger have a graceful moulding above a larger slab. 1920. (A later inscription by another hand.)

*386 Stations of the Cross in St Cuthbert's Catholic Church, Bradford, carved in low relief (originally painted in tempera) on Beer stone.

> The designs of the majority of these were after drawings made by Fr Desmond Chute: each 2 ft 6 in. square with a raised and gilt cross at the top. The titles, expressed very simply, are on the frames; the lettering in red. Latin is used on nine of the carvings, Greek on six. The roman caps are normal, the Greek have certain unusual characteristics – e.g. alpha has an angular crossbar, theta has a separated crossbar within the circle, kappa has sometimes a tall vertical, and the 'N's have sharp angles. Details are given below. 1921–24.

>> I 'Jesus is condemned to death'
>> The Latin words are central, on either side of a column, divided thus
>>> MORT / EM AU-
>>> TEMC / RUCIS
>> SPQR is on the base of the seat of Pilate (who is giving Jesus the 'thumbs down').

II 'He receives his cross'
ECCE LIGNUM CRUCIS is placed neatly like a postage stamp.

III 'Jesus falls'
SI FILIUS DEI ES is sited almost as if being said by the soldier.

IV 'He meets his mother'
MULIER VENIT HORA is placed centrally like a caption.

V 'Simon aids him'
TANTAE MOLIS ERAT is sited simply across the top.

VI 'Veronica comforts him'
DEDIT QUOD SUUM, small, again like a caption at the top.

VII 'Again he falls'
SEPTIES CEDIT JUSTUS in a block sited like a stamp.

VIII 'He tells women how to weep'
Five Greek words fill spaces at the top.

IX 'He falls again'
Four strong Greek words in a wide space: and CRUCIT EUM, very small by the edge.

X 'He is stripped'
Three Greek words tucked in at the top.

XI 'He is nailed'
Greek words in a strong block between the arm of Jesus and that of the workman hammering.

XII 'He dies'
INRI rather naively spaced at the top, and six Greek words boldly placed across the panel, the siting dependent on the horizontal line of the soldier's spear and the space above the horse's head.

XIII 'His mothers woe' (no apostrophe)
Three Greek words dividing the panel into carefully proportioned areas.

XIV 'He is entombed'
Five Greek words crammed into a narrow space near the ceiling of the tomb.

386A/P Inscription on the foot of a tall bas-relief of St Anthony of Padua at St Cuthbert's R.C. Church, Bradford: ORA PRO NOBIS.

c.1924.

*387 Circular tablet of Portland stone in Winchester Cathedral, in memory of Brigadier-General RONALD CAMPBELL MACLACHLAN, D.S.O., 1872–1917, within a laurel wreath, at the top of which is carved the D.S.O.

Fine caps contrasted with lower case. (No. 372 is immediately above.) 1921.

388 Portland headstone, with inscription in Latin, in memory of LENA MILMAN, 1862–1914, only daughter of Sir Bryan Milman.

1921.

*389 Tablet of Portland stone, letters in red and blue, surmounted by a coat of arms, over the doorway leading to the gallery, All Saints, Thorney Hill, Bransgore, Christchurch, Hants.

> 'We fought for England in the war of 1914–1918, and wounded and sick found at Avon Tyrell healing and a home.' The inscription runs on below in red italic: 'This stone is set here in token of our love and gratitude. Four hundred officers of the New Zealand Expeditionary Force.' Below the arms, neatly integrated with the stonework, the motto ONWARD on a bold ribbon forms a top for the inscription.
>
> 34 × 14; 1922. (See also 97 and 340A)

389A Exhibition piece: MATER AMABILIS ORA PRO NOBIS.

> Plus two flowers and a leafy decorated 'A'.
>
> R 2 × 42; 1921.

390 Marble tablet, with inscription in French, in Cambrai Cathedral, in memory of Lieut. EDWARD WILLIAM HORNER, 18th Hussars, 1888–1917 of Mells, Somerset, killed in action, November 1917.

> R 24 × 18; 1921. (See also 338)

390A/P War memorial on the outer wall of All Saints', St John's Wood, London N.W.8; twenty-five lines of names within a leafy frame.

> The memorial stone is integrated with the wall of the church by extending upwards the base moulding of the plinth. The names are assumed to have been cut in situ.
>
> 6 ft × 4 ft; c.1920.

391 Tablet beneath the war memorial (390A/P) on the outside wall near the west door of All Saints', St John's Wood, London, in memory of HARRY COULTER, 1887–1920 – 'Who having himself served in the war was foremost in raising this memorial to his Comrades'; followed, in italic, by 'He being dead yet speaketh'.

> 12 × 24; 1921.

392 Hopton-Wood stone tablet in All Saints', Debach, Woodbridge, Suffolk, in memory of MARIAN ALLBUTT, 1840–1910.

> Good caps, lower case and italic.
>
> R 15 × 28; 1921.

393 Gravestone of Hopton-Wood stone – ROSALIND MARY NASH 'lived sixteen years 1904–1920'.

> R 6 × 3; 1921.

*394 War memorial at the British Museum, incised on a pilaster beside the door. This, like the foundation stone of the Edward VII Galleries cut in 1911, is a fine example of integration of inscriptional work into a classical setting. Seven lines of bold caps span the stone, the date larger. Then follow the well-known words by Laurence Binyon in smaller caps, justified to the left, 'They shall grow not old …'. Below is a recessed wreath of laurels, gathered, unusually, at the top.

> 36 × 48; 1921. (See also 220)

395 Latin inscription on the wall by the steps leading to the Lady Chapel, Downside
Abbey, Bath, in memory of EDMUND BISHOP, d.1917.

> Below a chi-rho and alpha and omega (the 'A' with a chevron-like stroke across) runs a
> long inscription, partly centred, partly justified to the left, and of great interest and
> liveliness of layout, contrasting the severity of the lines of simple caps. The 'Q's are well
> swung out.
> c.48 × 36; 1921.

*396 War memorial cross at Trumpington, Cambridge.

> This tall cross, sited by the road and at the end of the drive to Trumpington Hall, is one
> of Gill's finest works. The sculptural treatment of arches round the base is characteristic –
> also the arches and interlinked panels at the foot of the shaft, within which the names are
> cut, justified to the left, and with Maltese crosses above and below. Within the base
> arches – 'For liberty and justice', the dates, and 'Men of Trumpington who gave their lives
> in the Great War' – with one example of joined letters HE to get the spacing right. In the
> arches at the foot of the shaft, a Virgin and Child with a crib and a bunch of flowers in a
> pot on a shelf; St George wearing a 'tin hat', killing a dragon below the 'Manus Dei' and
> with a bound damsel standing by; another with St Michael; and a tired soldier with rifle
> on his shoulder, marching past a cross. (Of this figure Mrs Pemberton of Trumpington
> Hall said to Gill, 'His right arm looks rather long', and received the reply, 'Yes, it felt like
> that'.) 1921.

*397 War memorial at Dunmow, Essex.

> This tall monument stands at the junction of three roads and responds to the siting in the
> form of a three-sided pillar topped by a cross at each side below a projecting arch.
> Sculpturally it is deceptively successful, the sides being concave and battered. It stands on
> three steps. The names are carved in caps on one concave face; memorial inscriptions
> below on the base, beginning 'Remember …' in large caps; 1924.

*398 War memorial of Hopton-Wood stone in the ante-chapel of New College,
Oxford.

> This grand work, framed in a big classical moulding, spans almost the whole wall. It is
> topped by three lines of 3 in. caps in red, the last of these widely spaced to fill the line.
> The words are unusually comprehensive – 'who died serving their country during five
> years of war 1914–1919 by land, by sea / and in the air, in Flanders, in France, in Italy, in
> Macedonia, in Gallipoli, in Palestine, in Mesopotamia, in all places to / which they were
> called, men worthy of all they learned here and an example to all those who come after
> them.' Then follow 228 names in full, in twenty-one lines of blue, 1 in. caps, year by year,
> the dates gilded. Being justified to the left in E.G.'s usual way, the spaces at the right vary
> greatly. In italic at the foot 'Also of … Lay Clerk, & … Servants of the College.'
> c.27 ft × 4½ ft; 1921. (See also 545)

399 War memorial tablet of Portland stone in the entrance hall of the Slade School
of Fine Arts, Gower Street, London.

> R 34 × 24; 1921.

399A/P War memorial in Ashbourne Church, Derbyshire; a large wall tablet (for
which the architect was A.W. Pearson, partner of Dr Charles Holden). Headed
with the single word REMEMBER in large caps in red, between the dates in black.

> The memorial inscription is designed to span exactly in two lines across the whole panel.
> Below are four columns of names in black in E.G.'s usual arrangement. Above is a fine

ON WARD

We fought for England
in the war 1914-1918
and wounded and sick
found at Avon Tyrrell
healing and a home.
This stone is set here in
token of our love and gratitude ❧ Four hundred
Officers of the New Zealand
Expeditionary Force.

37   Memorial at *All Saints, Thorney Hill, Bransgore,*
Hants, 1922 (389).

38   *War memorial at Great Dunmow, Essex,* 1921
(397).

coloured Sherwood Foresters' badge in bas-relief, the motto ribbon 'Notts & Derby' vigorously done. c.1921.

400 Cruciform gravestone at All Saints, Bisham, Marlow, Bucks., of JOHN HARRY SEPTIMUS KELLY, d.1921, aged four.

> The bold base bears the inscription, partly in Greek: the simple Latin cross, slightly tapered, bears a bas-relief fish. On the west face in caps – 'Go thy way, thy son liveth'.
> 1921.

401 War memorial panel of Euville stone in red and blue caps at St Dominic's Priory, Southampton Road, London, N.W.5. The inscription runs: A.D. 1914–1919. A STONE OF REMEMBRANCE FROM THE SOIL OF FRANCE. PRAY FOR THE MEN OF THIS PARISH WHO DIED IN THE WAR.

> The names are in thirteen lines of caps, in red, below which in blue are two lines of Lawrence Binyon's poem, but alas misquoted as 'They shall not grow old …'. Except for the top three lines and the bottom two, all are justified to the left. A very distinguished work.
> 53 × 73; 1921.

401A Headstone in memory of ALFRED WRIGHT STEELE, d.1910 and of EDNA, his wife, d.1912. Also of their daughter EMILY ELIZABETH STEELE, d.1921.

> 20 × 30; Cut by E.G. and Joseph Cribb 1921.

401B Inscription: O YE FIRE AND HEAT BLESS THE LORD PRAISE HIM AND MAGNIFY HIM FOR EVER.

> R 9 × 17; 1922.

402 War memorial tablet of Hopton-Wood stone, St Agatha's, Coates, Fittleworth, Sussex.

> The semi-circular head contains a Latin cross; centred below are five names in caps; above, slightly larger and in red, 'Remember'; three lines below in red. Simple and distinguished, the panel nicely detailed at the corners.
> 24 × 19; 1922.

403 Headstone of Green Hornton stone in memory of HERVEY GEORGE STANHOPE FISHER, 1873–1921. (Brother-in-law of Vaughan Williams.)

> 1922.

403A/P Oak panels incorporated into the pulpit and lectern at Ealing Green church, London W.5, with symbols of the Evangelists in relief and pierced, with small caps on narrow ribbons, with the words:
   a. The winged lion of St Mark: INITIUM E / GELLII / U / FILII / TUM ES
   b. The winged bull of St Luke: QUONIAM QU / DEM UT / T CONATI / SU / OR / INARE / NARR
   c. The angel of St Matthew: LIBER / ONIS / F / ABRAHAM
   d. The eagle of St John: IN PR / CIP / ERAT / V / RBU / APUD / EUM

> The oak ribbons outdo E.G.'s heraldic motto ribbons in their ingenious convolutions.
> 9 × 20; 1922.

404 War memorial tablet of Hopton-Wood stone, commemorating employees of W. H. & F. J. Horniman & Company Ltd., formerly in the vestibule of the Head Office, Shepherdess Walk, London N.I.

> The names are justified to the left. The regiments are reduced to their minimum, such as 'Rif. Brig', 'Lond. R', 'R. Fus' …
>
> R 39 × 18; 1922.

405 Grave memorial of Hopton-Wood stone, in Kensal Green Cemetery, London, in memory of MARIGOLD, daughter of Winston and Clementine Churchill, 1918–1921.

> Originally an octagonal pillar (with a crucifix and a group of figures) sited on a square-based stone with an eleven-line inscription in bold raised caps similar to the carving at Ilkley in 1904 (40). 'Here lies / Marigold / Dear Child / of Winston / & Clementine / Churchill / Born Nov 15 / 1918 / Died Aug 23 / 1921 / RIP.' Now renewed 'V'-cut to the original layout and surmounted by a cross. There are some concessions to the needs of spacing and texture such as a small 'o' and joined letters, e.g. 'NT', 'NE'.
>
> 1922 and c.1992.

406 War memorial tablet of Hopton-Wood stone in the Royal College of Music, Prince Consort Road, London, S.W.7.

> Thirty-nine lines in 1 in. caps; names justified to the left, with 'Pro Patria' in a separate tablet below the cornice in 2½ in. caps.
>
> 30 × 57; 1922.

*407 Inscription on the war memorial gateway of Bath stone, Clifton College, Bristol, to the memory of 3063 Cliftonians who served and of 578 who fell in the World War I.

> The inscription comprises 550 names of 7,200 letters, divided on each side of this gate and cut direct on the wall. A verse is also cut in italic, 'From the great Marshal to the last recruit / These, Clifton, were thy self, thy spirit in deed, / Thy flower in Chivalry, thy fallen fruit, / And their immortal seed'. 1922.

408 Hopton-Wood stone war memorial plaque in the Memorial Hall, Worplesdon, Surrey, commemorating the building of the Hall in 1921 and those who fell in World War I.

> Seven lines of caps.
>
> R 17 × 23; 1922.

409 Memorial recorded in the *Inventory* as at St Martin, Westmeston, Sussex, in memory of PETER NEWNHAM, d.1916, aged 71.

> E.G.'s drawing shows a cross like holly leaves, but on the site is a calvary with lead-filled letters unlikely to be by him. 1922.

410 Mural tablet of Hopton-Wood stone in Holy Cross Church, Gilling East, Richmond, Yorks., in memory of THOMAS PERCY PEMBERTON, 1833–1921, M.A., J.P., Vicar of the Parish 1870–1901. And of Captain FRANCIS PEMBERTON, killed in 1914.

This is the usual fine example of red and black caps and lower case in fifteen lines – but, unusually, centred. It is flanked by E.G.'s typical pilasters below a cambered cornice. (cf 312)

42 × 38; 1922.

411 Mural tablet, with inscription in Latin (in the *Inventory* as being at Ditchling) in memory of OLOF ALICE JOHNSTON, d. 11 February, 1917. A sister of Edward Johnston.

1922.

412 Inscription on slate in caps for a sundial for Lord Carmichael: GLORIA IN ALTISSIMIS DEO and IN TERRA PAX ... now in the Tate Gallery.

R 10 × 70 and 6 × 32; 1922.

413 Inscription on Portland stone: HOMINES DIVITES IN VIRTUTE / PULCHRITUDINIS STUDIUM HABENTES / ... Now in the Tate Gallery.

Three lines of different lengths, and PULCHRITUDINIS rather crowded. (Ecclesiasticus 44.6 – 'Rich men furnished with ability, living peaceably in their habitations.') Commissioned by Lord Carmichael.

R 9 × 35; cut by E.G. 1922.

414 Tablet on south wall of Amiens Cathedral, the inscription in French and Latin, in memory of RAYMOND ASQUITH, 1878–1916, Lieutenant, Grenadier Guards, killed in action at Guinchy, 15 September 1916. The inscription was phrased by his widow, Katharine Asquith, assisted by Hilaire Belloc. (See Plate XII in the *Inventory*.)

Fourteen lines, largely in lower case, very distinguished, and justified to the left – apart from the name and O ORIENS SPLENDOR. At the foot in one line of italic, very condensed, and with two upper-case 'R's – 'Gloriae memoriposuit conjux' – and an uncommon 'Æ'.

25 × 18; 1922. (See also 338)

*415 Sundial of Portland stone at Ditchling, Sussex, with an inscription in memory of ANTHONY WALLIS, 1879–1919.

With a well-detailed corner treatment to the square pillar.

Ht. c.39; 1922.

416 Slate tablet set on a Portland stone frame surmounted by a coat of arms, on south wall at St Dunstan, Mayfield, Sussex, in memory of APSLEY PHILIP TREHERNE, 1872–1922 also of GEORGINA WELDON, 1837–1914, daughter of Morgan Treherne of Gate House, Mayfield.

36 × 26; 1922.

416A/P War memorial at Balliol College, Oxford, in the form of seven cast bronze panels fixed to the wall within arches in the passage outside the chapel.

Raised lettering in upper and lower case, to take into account the slanting light from the doorway in the rather dark situation. The 190 names are interestingly arranged, dating from 'Matriculated in 1884' etc., with places of death, contracted where space demanded,

e.g. 'Mesop'. A daunting historical document in an unassuming situation. The architect was Macdonald Gill.
c. 60 × 24; 1922. (See also 233 and 516)

417 Incised inscription on small oak tablet in memory of ... DRAPER.

1922.

*418 War memorial of Portland stone, now in the hall of Leeds University Arts block, depicting Christ driving the money changers out of the temple. Along the cornice is inscribed, in caps, a passage adapted from the Vulgate version of St James's Epistle, 5.1; AGITE NUNC DIVITES PLORATE ULULANTES IN MISERIIS VESTRIS ... The right-hand panel carries a nine-line inscription, from St John's Gospel, 2.15: ET CUM FECISSET QUASI FLAGELLUM DE FUNICULIS ...

Several letters are combined to let the text fit the space above the dog with the flaming torch. 'L.S.D.' is carved on the accounts ledger held by one of the figures (i.e. pounds, shillings and pence).
6 ft × 16 ft; 1923.

419 Mural tablet of Hopton-Wood stone in the cloister at New College, Oxford, in memory of Sir HENRY ERLE RICHARDS, K.C.S.I., K.C., M.A., B.C.L., 1861–1922.

Twelve lines of caps and lower case, centred.
19 × 29; 1923.

420 Hogsback of Portland stone, St Michael, Wilsford, nr Amesbury, Wilts., in memory of WYNLAYNE, wife of Oliver William Foster LODGE, d. 1922. 'Her body was loveliness and her mind love.'

On the reverse of this stone Sir Oliver Lodge, 1878–1955, is commemorated, but this inscription was carved by Sydney Sheppard, 1956. Beneath it, however, is an inscription, JOURNEYS END IN LOVERS MEETING, which was cut earlier by E.G., reflecting Sir Oliver Lodge's belief in spiritualism. Distinguished by arches along the sides, the stone also contains a verse,

We have no more to ask for, sweet,
No gift from out the bitterest sky.
This is the limit of defeat.
And more of this I cannot die.

On one end a cross, at the other an owl on a branch. 1923. (See also 421)

421 Slate tablet with figures in low relief, on the north wall, St Michael, Wilsford, nr Amesbury, Wilts., in memory of WYNLAYNE, wife of Oliver William Foster LODGE of Upper Holcombe, Painswick, d. 1922.

An italic inscription beside the figures.
R 31 × 13; 1923. (See also 420)

422 Alabaster tablet in Chichester Cathedral in memory of HENRY HOLDING MOORE, 1839–1911, for forty-four years sacristan of the Cathedral – and E.G.'s father-in-law.

Signed on the frame, E.G. at the bottom right corner, and at the bottom left a cross, with the lower part of the shaft forming a 'D'.
R 10 × 19; 1923. (See also 568)

423 Headstone of Chambon stone with Hopton-Wood stone panel inserted, in memory of AGNES ELIZABETH MURRAY, 1894–1922, daughter of Prof. Gilbert and Lady Mary Murray, buried near Clermont Ferrand, Puy-de-Dôme, France.

Caps and lower case, and 'peace on earth, goodwill towards men'.
R 12 × 20; 1923.

424 Celtic Cross in Portland stone at Logie Coldstone, Dinnet, Grampian, in memory of JOHN CHRISTOPHER CARTER, d.1923, aged 9.

On the back, is carved, in nine lines, 'He pleased God and was beloved of him – yea speedily was he taken away lest that wickedness should alter his understanding or deceit beguile'. Wis. c.4 (i.e. The Wisdom of Solomon, 4.11) 1923. (See also 151)

425 A cross with a crucifix in relief, flanked by two angular-topped headstones, St Mary, Gilston, nr Harlow. They are of Hopton-Wood stone and (l to r) in memory of: REGINALD EDEN JOHNSTON, 1847–1922, with a low relief of the B.V.M., GEOFFREY STEWART JOHNSTON, 1889–1915, with a crucifix; and ROSE ALICE JOHNSTON, 1854–1907, with a low relief of St John the Evangelist.

The cross tapers slightly, and is set in a heavy square base. The inscriptions are in caps and lower case, the names placed naturally and asymmetrically. 1923.

426 Hopton-Wood stone tablet with coat of arms over, at East Carlton, Market Harborough, Leicester, in memory of the Rt Hon. NATHANIEL, BARON LINDLEY, P.C., F.R.S., 1828–1921 and his wife, d.1912.

Eighteen lines; done 'for Charles Holden'. A very distinguished memorial to 'the last created and the last surviving Sergeant at Law'.
R 31 × 30; 1923.

*427 Marble tablet at the entrance to the Chapter House, Westminster Abbey, in memory of WALTER HINES PAGE, 1855–1918, Ambassador of the United States of America to the Court of St James's, 1913–1918.

Nine lines of caps, then at the foot, 'The friend of Britain in her sorest need', with the four 'R's as capitals within the italic. (See Plate XIII in the Inventory.)
R 23 × 17; 1923.

428 Portland headstone with a steeply gabled top at Ringwould, Kent in memory of MARY CUMING, 1912–1921.

It is surmounted by a low relief of the Holy Child, between the words 'and a little child shall lead them'. 1923.

429 Portland headstone in Willesden Jewish Cemetery, London N.W.10, for the grave of SIEGMUND ALFRED SCHNAPPER, 1864–1922.

Pilasters at the side; caps and lower case. 1923.

430 Brass tablet in Stowe School, Bucks., to commemorate the occasion on 26 June 1923 when, on behalf of the Trustees of the Agenda Club, Sir Owen Seaman

placed in the keeping of the school a Samurai sword, 'forged by the armourer Yasatura, AD811, to be a symbol of service and a Challenge to Endeavour'.

R 11 × 14; 1923.

431 Foundation stone of the former Royal Northern Hospital, Manor Gardens, Holloway Road, London, laid by the Lady Patricia Ramsay.

1923.

431A/P Stone at the former Royal Northern Hospital to mark the opening by the Prince of Wales (later King Edward VIII).

1923. (See also 431, 431B/P, 437 and 456A–C/P)

431B/P Stone at the former Royal Northern Hospital to mark the opening of one part by Princess Louise, Duchess of Argyll.

A fine monogram of R.N.H. with the 'R' reversed, four lines of large caps.
c. 36 × 15; 1924.

432 Gravestone in Kensal Green Cemetery, London, in memory of the poet ALICE MEYNELL, d.1922.

Now fallen and partly broken. 1923.

433 Tablet in the Chapel of the Guards depot, Caterham, Surrey, commemorating the gift of Colours carried by the 1st Battn Coldstream Guards, 1857–1872 and presented in memory of Major-General Sir GEOFFREY FEILDING, K.C.B., C.M.G., D.S.O.

Ten lines of caps and lower case.
R 16 × 21; 1923.

434 Monument of Portland stone in memory of MAURICE HEWLETT, Poet, 1861– 1923.

> What then? To fold the hands
> Your work-hour over and done.
> Knowing you leave your lands
> The better for your son.
> Thankful he stands
> To reap what you have sown.

The italic has capital 'R's.
R 22 × 15; 1923.

435 Hopton-Wood octagonal pillar with sculptured group of Madonna & Child with four girls, at Northwood, Middlesex, in memory of CONSTANCE EVELYN TYSER, 1884–1922.

This is set on well-proportioned square-plan bases with the inscription similar to Marigold Churchill's memorial (405).
R 15 × 11; 1923.

436 Foundation stone for the chapel of the Royal Russell School, near Croydon, laid by the Prince of Wales (later King Edward VIII).

> Four lines of caps. 1924.

*436A/P Inscription round the entablature of Oxford House, Royal Russell School, Coombe Lane, Croydon.

> In 10 in. caps this long Latin inscription is one of the grandest Gill ever carved. The words are carefully divided to respond to the five faces of the entablature, CHRISTUM COMITA – MUR / CHRISTUM SEQUIMUR CHRISTUM / HABE – MUS ITINERUS DUCEM. The 'U's are still rather flat-bottomed and the 'M's have different angles. It is an excellent example of E.G.'s response to architecture. Architect, Sir Aston Webb.
> c. 35 ft long; 1924. (See also especially 436 D/P)

436B/P War memorial inscription on panel below a window on the south face of the Dining Hall, Royal Russell School.

> Seven lines of caps, centred. 1923.

436C/P Inscription on panel below a window on the south wall of the Dining Hall, Royal Russell School, recording the opening by the Prince of Wales.

> Seven lines of caps centred. 1923.

*436D/P Inscription cut below the cornice within the porch of the tower of the Royal Russell School Chapel.

> This neatly extends above three arches, the words devised to phrase well on each section – 'This tower / was erected in grateful recognition of / fifty years / service as / Treasurer of the schools from 1874 to 1924 / of the Rt. / Honourable Samuel Hope-Morley 1st Baron Hollendon / of Leigh'. (The Hope-Morley family were benefactors of the schools for several generations, the foundation now being known as the Purley Trust.) Architect, Sir Aston Webb.
> c. 15 ft. long; 1924.

437 War memorial tablets for the Borough of Islington on the street front of the former Royal Northern Hospital, Manor Gardens, Holloway Road, London N.7.

> Over the names in large caps is a general dedicatory text (with an ungainly 'M'). The 1260 names are in columns below, interestingly arranged: the initials of the individuals are cut to the left of each list of surnames, which are set out with the first letter of the name providing the vertical rhythm. By this means a lively, double 'unjustified' effect is obtained. Cut in situ, 1924.

438 Gravestone in Boulogne in memory of the poet and playwright HERBERT TRENCH, 1865–1923.

> Simple caps.
> R 6 × 25; 1923.

439 Inscription: O WANELESS ONE THAT ART THE CORE / OF EVERY HEART'S UNKNOWN DESIRE / TAKE BACK THE HEARTS THAT BEAT NO MORE.

> R 6 × 35; 1923.

39 *Gravestone of Wynlayne Lodge, Wilsford, Wilts., 1923 (420).*

40 *Royal Russell School, Addington, Croydon, Surrey,* 10 in. *letters on the cornice, 1924* (436A/P).

440 Memorial tablet of zinc for the Children's Hospital, Brighton, recording the gift of money to the hospital in 1922 in memory of ANNE HALL.

> No trace of this now.
> R 18 × 15; 1923.

441 War memorial tablet of Portland stone, with coat of arms at the top left corner, in Sir Roger Manwood's School, Sandwich, Kent.

> Ten lines, caps and lower case with occasional touches of wit, such as an extended 'g', in red and blue with dots between words counter-changed: 'Death is swallowed up in victory'. The motto ribbon is interestingly taken up beside the shield. 1924.

442 Inscription on a sundial: PENSA CHE QUESTO DI MAI NON RAGGIORNA.

> The background is of five arches of different widths. The 'V' in the figures has the first stroke extended in a flower. In QUESTO the 'O' was re-cut replacing an 'A', hence the spacing. Now in the Tate Gallery.
> R 18 × 15; 1924.

443 Small silver plate for a library table in the Overseas Club (now Royal Over-Seas League), St James's Street, London, recording the gift of the table in memory of the Hon. CHARLES THOMAS MILLS, Lieut., Scots Guards, killed in action October 1915.

> R 7 × 4; 1924.

443A/P Memorial stone at 'The Grand Cross' on the Downs at Plumpton, Sussex: 'Battle of Lewes May 14th 1264'. Erected by the Brighton and Hove Archaeological Club.

> Now vandalised. 1924.

444 Portland headstone in Brookwood Cemetery, Woking, in memory of ERNEST SYRETT, d.1906 and of MARIAN SYRETT, d.1923.

> Destroyed in the course of land reclamation and tree planting.
> R 12 × 11; 1924.

445 Base of cross of Portland stone in memory of LOUISE SHAW, 1867–1923.

> Inscription in caps and lower case; the cross tapered slightly. 'Thou hast loved righteousness and hated iniquity: Wherefor [sic] God, even thy God, hath anointed thee with oil of gladness above thy fellows.'
> 51 in. high; 1924.

446 Camber-arch headed memorial of Portland stone at St Mary, Storrington, Sussex, 'to the beloved memory of' PEGGY SUTTON, 1885–1923.

> Lower case roughly centred, and 'Sub umbrae alarum tuarum' in italic freely sited below. A charming stone.
> R 14 × 14; 1924.

447 Wall tablet in Brighton, the inscription surmounted by a carving of dolphins, for the site of Russell House, Grand Junction Road, Brighton, occupied by RICHARD RUSSELL, M.D., F.R.S., from 1754 until his death in 1759.

This was the first of several similar tablets commissioned by the Corporation of Brighton. (Others were: Nos 458, 459, 493, 494, 502, 525 and 551.) Cut first in Portland, replaced in Hopton-Wood in 1933, now replaced afresh in inferior work.

24 × 18; 1924.

448 Sculptured profile portrait and inscription in the foyer of St Martin's Theatre, Shaftesbury Avenue, London: REMEMBER MEGGIE ALBANESI AN ARTIST WHO DIED IN THE SERVICE OF THE THEATRE DECEMBER 9 1923 R.I.P. At the bottom left hand corner 'Given by Basil Dean'.

In caps of three sizes.
R 28 × 14; 1924.

*449 Funeral urn in Willesden Jewish Liberal Cemetery, Pound Lane, London N.W.10, with inscription on base, in memory of WALTER MORTIMER RONALDS, 1902–1924.

Rather like a tiny font, with carvings round the bowl; 18 in. high with recess for ashes.
R 6 × 7; 1926.

450 This item is in the *Inventory* as a cross-base in memory of WILLIAM MOODIE, d.1923 aged 76; a pencil and wash design is dated 1924.

The grave, however, in the Roman Catholic churchyard at Fordingbridge, Hants, is marked by a cross with a poor lead-filled inscription. Evidently E.G.'s design was not used.

451 Inscription on Beer stone: DILIGE + DEUM / ET + FAC + QUOD + VIS. (Love God and do what you will.)

Gill endorsed the rubbing. 'Top line: black and red (alternate letters) blue "dot". Bottom line: blue with red "dots".' Top line 1⅝ in.; bottom 1⅛ in. The 'M' has a short angular centre, surprisingly. Cut for Mrs Wertheim.
R 3 × 14; 1924.

452 White marble tombstone at St Margaret's, Ditchling, in memory of EDWARD COLLINS, 1854–1924.

Caps, with italics at the foot. 1924. (An additional inscription, 1942.)

453 War memorial in the Assembly Hall at Brighton Grammar School. Two oak panels about 8 ft × 4 ft with dates above and lists of names gilded and justified to the left. 1924.

453A/P Oak panel over the central door of the Assembly Hall at Brighton Grammar School with painted inscription associated with the war memorial (453).

*c.*12 ft × 1 ft 6 in.; 1924.

454 Inscription, surmounted by a bust of John Hunter (not E.G.'s work), on the entrance to the former St George's Hospital Medical School, Knightsbridge, London. FOUNDED MDCCLII / ST. GEORGE'S HOSPITAL MEDICAL SCHOOL.

Architects, Adams, Holden and Pearson. 1924.

455 Tablet of Capel-y-ffin stone, for a gate, LITTLE BELAN, for Mrs Wertheim.

> The first stone quarried and squared by E.G. at Capel-y-ffin.
> R 2 × 15; 1924.

456 Tablet of Hopton-Wood stone on a garden wall at Great Easton, Dunmow, Essex, in memory of HENRY GROUT, 1852–1924, H.G. Wells' gardener for thirty-one years.

> In italic, 'Every corner, every inch of this place is the better and richer for his work and care'.
> R 8 × 19½; 1924.

456A/P Portland stone commemorating the opening of the Royal Northern Hospital, by H.R.H. PRINCESS LOUISE Duchess of Argyll, 1924.

> Monogram of RNH, the 'R' reversed, and four lines of big caps justified to the left.
> A distinguished stone. 1924.

456B/P In situ carving over a door at the Royal Northern Hospital, a monogram of RNH and ST DAVID'S WING FOR PRIVATE PATIENTS. c.1924.

456C/P A similar carving over a door: ROYAL NORTHERN HOSPITAL NURSES' HOME.

> But in this case the second line of caps is embellished by charming extensions of the 'N' and 'M', and curved 'E's.

457 Hopton-Wood stone tablet in Bristol Cathedral, 'To keep in memory ADA VACHELL, Founder of The Bristol Guild of the Handicapped'.

> A woman made strong by God
> to give
> Love to the lonely
> Valour to the weak
> Comfort to the sorrowful
> MCMXXIII

> Somewhat casual spacing. At the top left hand a crossed crutch and sword, in relief and painted.
> R 18 × 25; 1924.

*457A The fourteen Stations of the Cross of Caen stone in the church of Our Lady and St Peter, Leatherhead, Surrey.

> Each is surmounted by a gilded maltese cross: and they are framed by a variety of rope mouldings. The titles, in lower case and in red, on the lower part of the frame, are very simply expressed, e.g. III Jesus falls, V Simon helps him, VIII The women weep for him, XIII His Mother receives Jesus, XIV Jesus is entombed.
> 20 × 18; 1924–5.

458 Wall tablet of Portland stone, the inscription surmounted by a carving of dolphins, for the Bedford Hotel in Brighton: CHARLES DICKENS 1812–1870, WAS A FREQUENT GUEST AT THIS HOTEL.

The old hotel was destroyed, and there is no plaque on the new building on the site.
20 × 19; 1924.

459 Wall tablet of Portland stone, inscription surmounted by dolphins, on 5
Percival Terrace, Brighton, where HERBERT SPENCER, 1820–1903, lived for some
years.

Now part of the Royal Promenade Hotel; replaced, but not by E.G.
R 16 × 19; 1924.

460 Inscription on pedestal of funeral urn of Istrian marble for the ashes of
WILLIAM AUGUSTUS CASSON, 1858–1924.

'The silent pathways of the night hold thy sweet spirit' in italic.
R 4 × 13; 1924.

*461 Hopton-Wood stone tablet in the Cloisters, Westminster Abbey in memory of
Sir FREDERICK BRIDGE, C.V.O., emeritus organist of Westminster Abbey 1882–
1918, b.1844 d.1924.

> Faithful in service
> Skilled in music
> Loving in friendship.

Red and black caps and lower case; the top five lines centred, the lower five justified to
the left. A simple, spaciously laid out inscription of great dignity, cut by E.G. himself.
R 30 × 36; 1925.

462 Foundation stone for the Whiteley Homes, Walton-on-Thames, laid by
Col. the Hon. A. G. Broderick, T.D., D.L., A.D.C., on behalf of the Trustees of the
Homes.

Simple caps. 1925.

463 Memorial in Hyde Park to W. H. HUDSON, 1841–1922. The dates are cut beside
Epstein's figure of Rima.

Along the paving stones round a long pool is carved in 5 in. caps, 'This sanctuary for birds
is dedicated to the memory of W. H. Hudson, writer and field naturalist'. Architects,
Adams, Holden and Pearson. 1925.

464 Headstone, with inserted panel, in memory of LOUISA CALTHROP, 1855–1925.
'For now we see through a glass darkly, but then face to face.'

1925. (See also 325)

465 Portland gravestone at All Saints, Corston, Bath, in memory of JULIET HELEN
WEITBRECHT, 1885–1924.

The top shaped in a series of five curves. (A drawing is endorsed by E.G. 'For Mrs Lionel
Hoare'.)
R 43 × 17; c.1926.

466 Headstone, surmounted by a cross, in memory of ANNIE HOUGHTON
DEARLE, d.1923 – 'who having spent her life in the fear of God and in doing what

she could, fell asleep Sept 4 1923 in her 46th year. He turneth the shadow of death into the morning.'

1925.

467 Portland headstone, St Michael, Wilsford, Wilts., in memory of VIOLET WATERHOUSE, eldest daughter of Sir Oliver and Lady Lodge; d.1924 aged 36.

Generously sized caps and seven lines of large italic, followed by 'She has rejoined her brother Raymond. Beloved of his family'.
R 16 × 20; 1925. (See also 420, 421)

468 Portland headstone, in memory of the art critic ARTHUR CLUTTON-BROCK, 1868–1924, at Godalming Old Cemetery, Farncombe. In caps, 'He sent his word and healed them'; followed in italic by:

> I a man by sickness worn
> On this day that Christ was born
> Turn again to this strange story
> Humility mixed with glory.

This would relate to the deceased having become a convert to Catholicism on Christmas Day 1923. A monogram is cut within the arched top.
R 28 × 22; 1925. (See also 316A/P and 482)

469 Hopton-Wood stone tablet for a house in Chelsea in which JOHN SINGER SARGENT R.A., 1856–1925, lived for twenty-four years and where he died in 1925.

Six lines of caps.
R 17 × 35; endorsed 'E.G. for Prof. Tonks.' November 1925.

470 Tablet of Capel-y-ffin stone on wall over main porch of St David's, Caldey Island, Tenby, commemorating the restoration of the church in 1925.

Two lines, caps and lower case, with MCMXXV, large and 'Laus Deo'. Three sizes of letter within the tablet 12 × 20; 1925. (See also 512)

471 Tablet of Capel-y-ffin stone at Brockham Green, Betchworth, Surrey, in memory of ROSINA JANE JOYCE, d.1924.

Simple caps.
R 12 × 20; 1925.

472 Ledgerstone of Portland stone, St Michael, Cumnor, Oxford, in memory of LILY DOUGALL, 1858–1923. 'He satisfieth the longing soul.'

Three lines of big caps, and four maple leaves for Montreal.
R 9 × 69; 1926.

473 In situ carving on pier in Cotham Church, Bristol, in memory of Revd Dr H. A. THOMAS, 1848–1924. 'Beloved Pastor of this church for 47 years.'

Eight lines of caps, then in italics, 'Great grace was upon him'. The layout is interesting – six lines centred below a corbel, three justified to the left but spanning the pier. One of the alternative designs showed a figure of Isaiah and the other, the accepted design, The Good Shepherd.
R 18 × 23; 1926.

41   E.G.'s drawing for a 'funeral urn' at *Willesden Cemetery*, 1926 (449).

42   *Memorial in the cloisters at Westminster Abbey, cut by Eric Gill himself; unusual but characteristic layout, 1925* (461).

43   In situ *carving on a pier at Cotham Church, Bristol*, 1926 (473).

473A Tablet of Portland stone on a wall on the Black Lion public house, Black Lion St, Brighton: DERYK CARVER, FIRST PROTESTANT MARTYR BURNT AT LEWES JULY 22 1555, LIVED IN THIS BREWERY. Commissioned by Brighton Council.

Letters now painted black, and a further stone added, not by E.G.
R 14 × 30; 1926.

473B/P Tablet commissioned by Brighton Borough Council on 55 Old Steyne, Brighton, to mark its association with Mrs FITZHERBERT.

Letters now painted red.
c. 24 × 18; c.1926.

474 Round-headed headstone of Portland stone in St Giles Cemetery, Huntingdon Road, Cambridge, in memory of FRANCIS DARWIN, 1848–1925. 'O ye humble men of heart, bless ye the Lord.'

An inscription below in similar style to his daughter Frances Cornford, d.1960, by another sensitive hand.
R 15 × 17; 1926.

474A/P A headstone similar to 474 in memory of HORACE DARWIN, 1851–1928 and his son ERASMUS, killed near Ypres.

Below, by another hand, a memorial to Ida Darwin, 1854–1940. 1928.

475 Hopton-Wood stone tablet in the south transept, St Michael, Cumnor, Oxford, in memory of LILY DOUGALL, 1858–1923.

The name in caps in red with an extended 'L' to fill the space, plus lines of interestingly mixed lower case and italic. WHATEVER IS TRUE IS GOD'S WAY OF REVEALING HIMSELF. L.D. A charming piece.
R 22 × 16; 1926. (See also 472)

476 Gravestone of Portland stone in memory of HELEN THORP AND JOSEPH PETER THORP.

R 16 × 16; cut by E.G., 1926.

477 Hopton-Wood stone tablet in the entrance hall of Fisher House, Cambridge, (the University R.C. Chaplaincy) in memory of PERCY FITZGERALD, d.1925.

Latin, twelve lines of caps, justified to the left; one line of italic at the foot.
R 25 × 30; 1926.

*478 Recumbent gravestone, St Nicholas, Brushford, Dulverton, Somerset, in memory of the Hon. AUBREY HERBERT, M.P., Captain, Irish Guards, 1880–1923. Son of Henry, 4th Earl of Caernarvon.

A cross in relief with two shields below the cross-bar and the motto ribbon crossing the vertical, then the lettering as a fine texture of bold caps divided thus: AUBR / EY HER / BERT B / ORN AP / RIL 3. 18 / 80 DIE / D SEPT / 26 1923. Then follows, in similar vein, by another sensitive hand, AND M / ARY HI / S WIFE / BORN A / PRIL 10 / 1889 DI / ED NOV / 28 1970. The shields bear the arms of Herbert, three lions rampant and a cross with a cross superimposed. 1926.

479 Wooden panel with words painted in red and black, from St Thomas Aquinas:

'La Beauté / Divine est cause de / l'être de tout ce qui est. The beauty of God is the / cause of the being of all that is.'

> The French in roman caps, in black, alternating with the English in upper and lower case italic, in red.

> This was for the Victoria & Albert Museum's Circulation Department for their travelling exhibitions. They also published a collotype reproduction in 1926 as No. 4 of four Lettering Sheets.
> 22 × 30; 1926.

*479A Hopton-Wood stone panel with a quotation from St Thomas Aquinas: EX DIVINA PVLCHRITVDINE ESSE OMNIVM DERIVATVR.

> Roman capitals, incised and coloured red, blue and black. The final 'R' swung out. This was done for the Victoria & Albert Museum's Circulation Department for their travelling exhibitions. The museum published a collotype reproduction of it, the letters in red, black and blue, in 1926 as No. 3 of four Lettering Sheets.
> R 14 × 20; 1926.

480 Foundation stone for the College Chapel, St Oswald's, Ellesmere College, Shropshire.

> Ten lines of caps, with the date larger at the foot, and a fine shield in low relief within a shallow panel. Neatly related in dimensions to the brickwork.
> 30 × 41; 1926.

481 Hopton-Wood headstone in Radley Churchyard, near Abingdon, Berks., in memory of FLORENCE BRADSHAW, d. 1925 and of JOHN GERALD BRADSHAW, d. 1931, founder of Packwood Haugh.

> A maltese cross in low relief at the top, the lettering within a moulded frame.
> R 17 × 20; 1926. (See also 500)

482 Portland headstone at Weybridge, in memory of JOHN ALAN CLUTTON-BROCK, 1842–1925; next to Mary Alice Clutton-Brock, d. 1915 (316A/P). Parents of Arthur Clutton-Brock (468).

> Plain caps with a sprig of laurel over.
> R 18 × 20; 1926.

483 Portland headstone, in memory of WILLIAM STEPHEN MARCHANT, 1870–1925.
> A cross over, the vertical stroke dividing JESU / MERCY. 1926.

484 Fascia-board lettered DOUGLAS CLEVERDON for his bookshop, formerly in Park Street, Bristol, painted by E.G. Oct. 30 – Nov. 1, 1926. Destroyed in an air raid during World War II.

> From the letters used on this board the type design Gill Sans was developed in 1927. (See Plate XVI in the *Inventory*.) (See also 484A, 528 and 718)

484A Zinc name-plate, 2 × 4½ in., originally above the bell-push at Douglas Cleverdon's bookshop in Bristol which was destroyed in World War II.

> 1926. (See also 484)

> (A reproduction of the rubbing will be found in the *Monotype Recorder*, 41:3 (1958), 15.)

485 Brass tablet on the west wall of the ante-chapel at Eton, with a crest and motto and a long inscription in Latin, letters engraved and filled in black and red: 'In piam memoriam LUDOVICUS HEATHCOAT AMORY' of Tiverton, killed in action in France 1918, aged 37.

> Followed by a Latin motto, in condensed italic in red.
> c. 24 × 9; 1926.

486 Inscription cut in the wall of the crypt at Downside Abbey, Bath, in memory of J. C. DENHAM PARKER d.1905 and ANTHONY PEREIRA d.1918, buried in the village cemetery.

> The *Inventory* item relating to Everard Green must refer to another site. c.1926.

487 Letter-box cover with the word LETTERS (the letters set one beneath the other) carved in wood for the house '4 Elms', Waltham St Lawrence, Berks. (now 'The Old Press'), occupied by Robert and Moira Gibbings, owners of the Golden Cockerel Press.

> R 7 × 1; 1926.

487A Foundation stone for Torbay Hospital laid 1926 by Mrs MARIAN ROWCROFT, the donor, erected in memory of her parents Sir EDWARD PAYSON WILLS Bt, K.C.B. and MARY ANN his wife, of Bristol.

> Nine lines of caps and lower case elegantly disposed.
> R 48 × 22; 1926. (See also 514A)

487B/P Sculpture above the door at 'The Old Press', Waltham St Lawrence, Berks., with four elms and a cockerel, and 'R & MG. 1927'.

488 Hopton-Wood stone tablet in memory of ANNE ELIZABETH CHANCE, d.1925.

> Roman and Italic.
> R 15 × 13; 1927.

489 Headstone surmounted by a crucifix, at Harlow, Essex in memory of MARIA ANNA GILBEY, 1897–1927 of Mark Hall, Harlow.

> 1927. (cf also 507)

490 Memorial panel of Hopton-Wood stone for All Saints, Pimlico, London, in memory of the painter AMBROSE McEVOY, 1878–1927; destroyed when the church was bombed during World War II.

> c.1927.

491 Tablet in memory of Major NICHOLAS ROTHESAY MONTAGUE STUART WORTLEY, M.C., Royal Flying Corps, 1892–1926.

> 1927.

491A Foundation stone for the ROYAL WESTMINSTER OPHTHALMIC HOSPITAL, High Holborn, London, W.C.1., laid by H.R.H. the Duke of Connaught K.G., 30th June 1927; now demolished.

Eleven lines of caps in two sizes; the last justified to the left.
20 × 30; 1927. (See also 491B)

492 Hopton-Wood stone tablet in St Martin's, Scarborough, in memory of Dr
FRANK WILLIAM ALBION GODFREY, 1860–1925.

A spacious centred inscription of nine lines of red and black caps of singular distinction
to, 'A beloved physician, a trusted friend for whose life and service we give thanks'. There
is one case of an unexpected pair of joined letters 'NK' in the last line, and a lovely
flowered finish to the 'Y' of 'Godfrey'. c.1927.

492A/P Tablet in St John's, Knutsford, Cheshire, recording the use of the church 'by
the Ex Servicemen of all ranks training for Holy Orders in the prison building
which stood opposite to it'.

Eight lines, largely in lower case, and with italic at the foot. 'The Lord strengthened them
out of Sion. The Lord send you help from the Sanctuary.' c.1923.

493 Tablet of Portland stone, the inscription surmounted by dolphins, on 31
Buckingham Rd, Brighton, in memory of AUBREY BEARDSLEY, 1872–1898, who
was born in the house.

R 22 × 19; 1927.

494 Tablet of Portland stone, in Brighton, the inscription surmounted by dolphins
at 79 Buckingham Road, Brighton, in memory of E. J. MARSHALL, Headmaster of
Brighton Grammar School 1861–1899, d.1899.

R 22 × 19; 1927.

495 War memorial tablet of black marble, for the former entrance hall of the offices
of Crosse & Blackwell, Ltd, in Soho Square, London.

Recording thirty-seven names this is now covered by an oak tablet on which are the
names of those who fell in World War I and World War II. ('Crosse' was recut from
'Cross'.)
R 24 × 66; 1927.

496 Tablet of Hopton-Wood stone, St Michael's, Howick, Alnwick, Northumberland, in memory of Lady VICTORIA SYBIL MARY GRENFELL, 1878–1907,
daughter of 4th Earl Grey.

Good simple caps.
R 19 × 28; c.1927.

497 Portland headstone near White Nose cliff, Lulworth Cove, Dorset, in memory
of WALTER FRANZEN of New York, d. May 1927, aged 34. 'In the sunshine of a
spring morning he left the White Nose. He fell from the cliff at West Bottom
where the elder trees grow. He was known in lumber camps of virgin forests.
Wherever he went there were those to love his proud and solitary nature. The
glory of young men in their strength, and the beauty of old men in the grey head.
(Prov. XX, v 29)'

1927.

EX DIVINA PVLCHRITVDINE ESSE OMNIVM DERIVATVR

44   Hopton-Wood stone panel cut for the *Victoria & Albert Museum*, 1926 (479A).

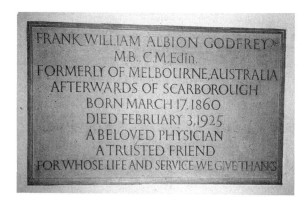

FRANK WILLIAM ALBION GODFREY
M.B., C.M.Edin.
FORMERLY OF MELBOURNE, AUSTRALIA
AFTERWARDS OF SCARBOROUGH
BORN MARCH 17, 1860
DIED FEBRUARY 3, 1925
A BELOVED PHYSICIAN
A TRUSTED FRIEND
FOR WHOSE LIFE AND SERVICE WE GIVE THANKS

45   Memorial at St Martin's, Scarborough, c.1927 (492).

E.J. MARSHALL.
HEADMASTER OF THE
BRIGHTON GRAMMAR
SCHOOL FROM 1861 TO 1899
CARRIED ON THE LAST
THIRTY-ONE YEARS OF
HIS WORK

46   *One of many similar tablets commissioned by Brighton Council, 1927 (494).*

498 Alphabet of capital letters incised on Hopton-Wood stone, for the Victoria & Albert Museum, London. (19½ × 21 in.). Now in the Tate Gallery.

> This now famous alphabet, within a simple moulded frame has many characteristics which were later superseded in E.G.'s workshop practice, e.g. a short central bar to 'E', a rather narrow 'G' with a high vertical, an 'R' with the downstroke propping up the bowl. The 'V' is at 'about 60°. Notably the junctions of the outer strokes of the 'M' with the central 'V' strokes arrive at different levels at the join. The accompanying notes mention that the letters are slightly deeper at the serifs.
>
> R 19 × 21; cut by E.G. and Laurie Cribb, 1927.

498A Alphabet of 3 in. capital letters in relief on Hopton-Wood stone, for the Victoria & Albert Museum, London. Now in the Tate Gallery.

> R 20 × 21; cut by E.G. and Laurie Cribb, 1927.

499 Portland headstone in Compton Cemetery, Guildford, Surrey, in memory of ETHEL ANN BURTON-BROWN, of Prior's Field, 1868–1927.

> A maltese cross in relief, then five spaciously arranged lines of caps, and, in italic, 'Her children rise up & call her blessed'.
>
> R 33 × 27; 1927.

500 Tablet of Portland stone, at Lapworth Church, Warwickshire, the inscription surmounted by a panel of the Madonna and Child in relief, 'In memory of FLORENCE BRADSHAW of Packwood Haugh, who worshipped here: 1895–1922'.

> Five lines of caps in two sizes; within the relief sculpture, arranged vertically, 'Mater amabilis', in caps. (See Pevsner, *Buildings of England: Warwickshire*, pl. 60.) 1927. (See also 481)

501 War memorial tablet of Hopton-Wood stone, St Michael and All Angels, Sopley, Hants, commemorating the restoration of the belfry and bells in 1927, and in memory of those 'Who gave their lives for England. May they rest in peace.'

> Thirty-three names arranged in mass, not columns.
>
> 33 × 34; 1927.

502 Wall tablet, the inscription surmounted by dolphins, on the Royal Cross Hotel, 100 Marine Parade, Brighton, commemorating GEORGE CANNING, Statesman, 1770–1827, who at one time lived there.

> Badly weathered, and colourfully painted now.
>
> R 18 × 20; 1927.

503 Tablet for house formerly at 60 Sidney Street, Cambridge, where CHARLES DARWIN lived in 1828. The tablet is now in the Cambridge and County Folk Museum because the house was destroyed.

> 7 × 16; 1927. (See also 504)

504 Tablet for house 22 Fitzwilliam Street, Cambridge, where CHARLES DARWIN lived 1836–7.

> R 9 × 17; c.1927. (See also 503)

505 Headstone in memory of Lieut.-Col. E. A. BALL, late Royal Warwickshire Regiment, 1848–1926.

1928.

506 Memorial tablet of Hopton-Wood stone in memory of JOHN BEAUMONT HOTHAM of Milne Graden, nr Coldstream, Berwickshire, 1874–1924.

After twenty-three years' service in the House of Lords he was appointed Clerk of the Senate in the first Parliament of Northern Ireland, 1921–4.
R 29 × 19; 1927.

507 Head- and footstone at Latton churchyard, Harlow, Essex, in memory of ANGELA GILBEY, d. April 1925.

This has bold and unusual classical detail, with arched top and scrolled sides. The lettering is of fine upper- and lower-case roman, centred.
R 16 × 21; 1928. (cf 489)

508 Wall tablet with an inscription in memory of AYLEN DE TAVORA LUIS DE FERNANDES, of Haddon Lodge, 1902–1921.

(Wrongly stated in the Inventory to be at Stourton, Wilts.) Surmounted by coats of arms with fine motto ribbons – Eton, Fernandes and another. 1928.

508A/P Hopton-Wood stone Credence shelf for the chapel at Pigotts: SICUT OCCULI. ANCILLAE IN MANIBUS DOMINAE SUAE +. 1 in. caps in red and blue.

c.1928.

509 Tablet of Hopton-Wood stone, St Nicholas, Poling nr Arundel, in memory of Sir HARRY JOHNSTON, G.C.M.G., K.C.B., D.Sc., Administrator, Soldier, Explorer and Naturalist, 1858–1927.

Seven lines of caps, and a line of italic: 'Vir fortis, audax, mitis, ingenio magno.'
R 14 × 20; 1928.

510 Portland headstone surmounted by a crucifix, in the Inventory as at Garstang, Lancs., in memory of MARY REEVES, d.1927 aged 67 years.

There is a pencil drawing of a female figure, for the back of the headstone, signed by E.G. 1928.

511 Memorial stone of Hopton-Wood stone in Bradford Cemetery for the ashes of CHARLES LAMBERT RUTHERSTON, 1866–1927, son of Moritz and Bertha Rothenstein.

A pencil drawing shows an elegant top and leafy thistle carving.
R 14 × 16; 1928. (See also 251)

512 Font of Bath stone in St David's, Caldey Island, Tenby, with inscription: NON POTEST INTRARE IN REGNUM COELORUM … (St John, 3).

1928. (See also 470)

*513 Hogsback gravestone with a carved crucifix in Portland stone at the Catholic Church of St Edmund, Abingdon, in memory of MONTAGU ARTHUR, 7th Earl of Abingdon, 1836–1928, High Steward of Abingdon.

Four lines of caps justified to the left. The memorial inscription to Lady Abingdon is by another hand, c.1942.

R 9 × 41; 1929.

514 Circular tablet of Portland stone, letters in relief: B.B.C. (British Broadcasting Company), for the outside wall of the original headquarters of the B.B.C. in Savoy Hill, London.

(The title was changed to 'British Broadcasting Corporation' in January 1927.)

R 17 × 16; 1928.

514A Panel of Hopton-Wood stone in Torbay Hospital recording the gratitude of the Governors to Mrs Ella Marian Rowcroft of Pilmuir, Torquay, for the gift of the hospital and Nurses' Home.

Thirteen lines of caps, centred except for two lines justified to the left. 1928. (See also 487A)

515 Hopton-wood head- and footstone (near Oxford) in memory of FRANCIS ELRINGTON BALL, Litt.D., d.1928. Also of FLORENCE EGLANTINE his wife, d.1913.

This has fine architectural details for the arched cornice; the lettering is in caps and lower case, and centred. 1929.

516 Bronze tablet in the ante-chapel of Balliol College, Oxford, in memory of HENRY HERBERT ASQUITH, Earl of Oxford & Asquith, 1852–1928.

The original design had flourished caps for 'A', 'N', 'R', 'Q' and 'X' – but these were tamed in the final design, which is singularly uninteresting.

R 14 × 28; 1929. (See also 233 and 416A/P)

517 Hogsback gravestone with footstones near the south transept of Peterborough Cathedral in memory of Canon JOHN EDWARD STOCKS, D.D. 1843–1926.

On the end is, 'Withdraw not thy mercy from me, O Lord', in four lines of caps. 1929.

(A drawing was published in Sculptured Memorials & Headstones.)

518 Foundation stone on the wall near the entrance of the headquarters of the London Underground Railways, St James's Park Station, Broadway, Westminster, 1929. Architect, Charles Holden.

The letter-cutting was the joint work of E.G. and Laurie Cribb. 1929.

518A/P A similar stone to No.518 at London Underground Ltd., laid by 'Thomas Auton, Housekeeper, 1899–1929: for 43 years a servant of the companies'.

1929.

519 Hopton-Wood stone tablet in a library at Tirana, Albania, commemorating the gift of the library to the young people of Albania. The inscription runs: HANC BIBLIOTHECAM IN USUM POPULI ALBANI AEDIFICANDAM CURAVIT ELISABETHA COMTISSA DE CARNARVON. MANET IN MEMORIAM ET MATRIS … 1929.

R 16 × 22; 1929. (See also 565)

520 Designs for face and gnomon of a sundial for cottages at Chestnut Crescent, Witley, Surrey, for Sir Aston Webb.

> 28 × 27; 1928.

521 Portland cross on a substantial arched base in Stanmer Park, nr Brighton, in memory of JOCELYN BRUDENELL PELHAM, 6th Earl of Chichester, 1871–1926, also for FRANCIS GODOLPHIN HENRY PELHAM, 7th Earl, 1905–1926.

> The stone also has, 'All shall be well …' from *Revelations of Divine Love* by Julian of Norwich. The stone is pierced to form a cross, which is carved as a bas-relief tree of life, dividing the two inscriptions.
> R 15 × 18; 1929.

522 Headstone and large sculpture of an angel in Hopton-Wood stone, in Brompton Cemetery, London, in memory of HELEN ROSE PUSCH, 1874–1928, also of her sons FREDERICK LEOPOLD, Lieut. Irish Guards, D.S.O., killed in action at Loos 1916, aged 20 and ERNEST JOHN, 2nd Lieut. Royal Warwickshire Regt killed in action on the Somme 1916. 'And they shall be mine, saith the Lord of Hosts in that day when I make up my jewels.'

> A monumental work; over twenty lines of caps form a texture over the stone with pilasters at the sides. 1929. (Additional words were cut in 1940)

523 Portland headstone in Brompton Cemetery, London, in memory of EMILY ALICE WHITE, 1845–1922, and of FREDERICK ANTHONY WHITE 1842–1933 and EFFIE REDESDALE WHITE, 1876–1932 his second wife.

> Below the curved top is a rising sun. Fifteen lines of caps.
> R 22 × 25; 1929.

524 Exhibition piece – TU ES PETRUS ET SUPER …

> R 12 × 21; c.1929.

525 Wall tablet of Hopton-Wood stone, inscription surmounted by dolphins, on 20 Old Steyne, Brighton, where GIDEON ALGERNON MANTELL, Geologist, lived 1833–8.

> Letters now painted black.
> R 22 × 18; 1929.

526 Pierced celtic cross in memory of COLVILLE ADRIAN DE RUNE BARCLAY, 1869–1929 in Brookwood Cemetery, Surrey.

> The cross has a stylised tree on both sides, and raised letters, 'Crux Christi nostra corona' round the circle; leaves in the centre. 1929.

> (An additional inscription was cut in May 1930, in memory of his wife SARITA 1891–1935.)

527 Headstone at All Saints, Compton Greenfield, Bristol in memory of KOSSUTH ROBINSON, d.1928 and of his three sons, CLIFFORD KOSSUTH, EDWARD COLSTON and GEOFFREY WATHEN, 'sacrificed in War, 1915'.

> This has a many-curved top with a cross and leaves above the inscription, centred in caps; below in italic, 'Life for evermore'.
> 63 × 34; 1929.

IN MEMORY OF
SIR HARRY JOHNSTON
G.C.M.G., K.C.B., D.Sc.
ADMINISTRATOR SOLDIER
EXPLORER, NATURALIST
AUTHOR AND PAINTER
1858 – 1927
Vir fortis, audax, mitis, ingenio magno.

47   Memorial at St Nicholas, Poling, Sussex, 1928 (509).

JOCELYN
BRUDENELL
PELHAM
6TH EARL OF
CHICHESTER
DIED NOV 14
1926 AGED
33 YEARS

FRANCIS
GODOLPHIN
HENRY
PELHAM
7TH EARL OF
CHICHESTER
DIED NOV 22
1926 AGED
21 YEARS

48   Eric Gill's drawing for the memorial to two
members of the Pelham family, and a tree of life,
Stanmer Park, Brighton, Sussex, 1929 (521).

FOR THE REPOSE OF THE SOUL OF
...AGUE ARTHUR, 7TH EARL OF ABINGDON
...STEWARD OF ABINGDON
...N 13 MAY 1836 – DIED 10 MARCH 1928. R.I.P.

49   Eric Gill's drawing for the grave
of the Earl of Abingdon, St Edmund's,
Abingdon, 1929 (513).

125

527A/P DOMINUS VOBISCUM cut as a sample for Arnold Robinson, in connection with the headstone 527.

> 7 × 8; 1920.

528 White marble cross on a base of three steps primarily to CECILY ELEANOR GILL 1883–97 (E.G.'s sister) in the Extra-Mural Cemetery, Lewes Road, Brighton, with the base cut in memory of CICELY ROSE GILL, 1854–1929, wife of the Revd Arthur T. Gill, E.G.'s parents.

> The inscription is a very early use of Gill Sans and, unusually, lead-filled letters in the customary way with monumental masons, but set out in E.G.'s way justified to the left. 1929.

> A further inscription in 1933 commemorates the Revd ARTHUR TIDMAN GILL, 1933.

529 Portland headstone, with figure of a child with a toy engine carved in relief, in memory of JOHNNIE MANN, d.1925, aged 4½ years – 'To see the beauty of the Lord and to enquire in his temple'.

> 1929.

530 Portland head- and footstones in Brookwood Cemetery, Woking, with inscription in memory of HENRI SEE, 1862–1929 and MAY SEE, d.1880, within recessed panels.

> The stones are joined and shaped in the form of a double bed. ' – Wherefore they are no more twain but one flesh.'
> R 8 × 16 and 5 × 15; 1929.

531 Gravestone on Rogoa Island, off Samarai, Papua New Guinea, in memory of FRANCES MARY GILL, born 1 July 1926, died 1929, the daughter of Cecil and Nonie Gill.

> 14 × 15; 1929.

531A Carved headboard of an oak bed in Cambridge, Mass., U.S.A. consisting of three panels each containing a carving in relief with incised lettering above and beneath each carving. Left-hand panel: HIC NATI PER DOLORES AD CAPIENDA PER PARTVM VIRGINIS GAVDIA INENNARABILIA. Centre: HIC RENOVATVR IN AMORE SPONSALI GENVS HOMINVM MORTALE PER SPONSALIA CHRISTI ET ECCLESIA MIRIFICA COELICOLARVM IMMORTALE. Right-hand panel: HIC TANDEM OBRIGESCIMVS MORTE POENA PECCATI PER ADAE CVLPAM: PER RESVRRECTIONXTI PORTA SOLA VITE.

> For the two outer panels the lettering runs to three lines and is rather condensed. The overall effect is rich. The two outside panels: 12 × 10, the centre panel: 12 × 14. The relief carvings were done by E.G. at Capel-y-ffin. The bed was made by Romney Green in whose workshop at Christchurch, Hants, the inscriptions were also cut from drawings sent to him by E.G. Commissioned by Graham Carey. 1929.

532 Portland headstone at All Saints, Witley, Surrey, in memory of ARTHUR STANSFIELD DIXON of Birmingham, 1856–1929. Also of his children MARY DIXON, 1887–1922 and JAMES EVELYN DIXON, 1893–1916, killed in action near Beaumont Hamel, 1916.

HIC·RENOVATVR·IN·AMORE
SPONSALI·GENVS·HOMINVM

MORTALE·PER·SPONSALIA·
CHRISTI·ET·ECCLESIA·MIRIFIC
A·CŒLICOLARVM·IMMORTALE

51   Pillar memorial at Merton
College, Oxford, 1931 (558).

50   Detail of one panel of the
headboard of a bed, 1929 (531A).

This quietly classical stone has sixteen lines of small caps centred.

(The precedent for the detail of this stone is set by a fine headstone in the same churchyard in memory of Agnes Margaret Dixon 1865–1918, the letterforms and spacing of which are not of E.G.'s sort.)

At the foot is a later inscription for his wife Emily Gertrude d.1941.
54 × 29; 1929.

532A Inscription, incised on York stone, on a building in Chichester Rents, Chancery Lane, London, W.C.2: CHICHESTER, and CHICHESTER ESTATES CO.

R 2 × 13 and 4 × 12; 1930.

*533 Altar tombstone with inscriptions on two sides at Little Compton, Moreton-in-the-Marsh, Glos., in memory of The Rt Hon. FREDERICK LEVERTON HARRIS, P.C., 1864–1926. 3 in. caps and 2½ in. for, 'Nature I loved, and after nature art / I warmed both hands before the fire of life. / Thou callest. / I am ready to depart.' (Adapted from W.S.Landor.)

For the ends of this distinguished design, handsomely moulded, are a bas-relief of leaves, and a pelican. The quotation has certain letters joined.
R 11 × 62 and 11 × 62; 1930.

534 Hopton-Wood stone tablet in St Mary's, Bromfield, Shropshire, in memory of HENRY HILL HICKMAN, 1800–1830.

A very distinguished memorial with fine contrasts of letter forms; eight lines, then in italic of two sorts – 'This tablet is placed here at the initiative of the section of anaesthetics of the Royal Society of Medecine as a centenary tribute to the memory of the earliest known pioneer of anaesthesia by inhalation. Honour a Physician with the honour due unto him. AD 1930.'
R 33 × 28; 1930.

535 Hogsback stone in Kensal Green Cemetery, London, in memory of ANTHONY POLIMENI, 1844–1928.

A grand stone with four lines of caps, the name larger: PACEM IMPLORATE ANIMAE … E.G.'s note says, 'I think an inscription like this reads more easily if it begins with an accented first syllable (pácem rather than oráte). I suggest something longer than ANNO DOMINI to balance the longer 2nd date. I generally stick the month as well as the year and day all in the ablative. "Diem supremum abire" always sounds to me a little fatalistic, perhaps wrongly – Cathc metres – St Augustine's phrase, is so beautiful that I take every opportunity to use it. All the rhythms have been made more definite, ending with the fullest cursus – ∞ – o /.' On the ends of the stone, a cross and IVSTVS MEVS EX FIDE VIVIT – on this stone avoiding the use of 'J' and 'U' in Latin, rather unusually for E.G.
c. ½ × 73 and 8 × 11; 1930.

(Further inscriptions by another hand in English are on the other side.)

536 Hopton-Wood stone tablet re-erected in St George's, Camberwell, 1961, – 'We pray you remember the soul of CHARLES FREDERICK GURNEY MASTERMAN', 1873–1927.

A very fine inscription of fourteen lines surmounted by a camber arch with a casket in relief. It was formerly in St Stephen's, Walworth, which was destroyed by enemy action during World War II.

c. 35 × 26; 1930.

537 Ledgerstone of Portland stone in the private graveyard at St Michael and All Angels, Himley, Dudley, Staffs., in memory of JOHN JEREMY WARD, 1922–1929.

Seven lines of large caps.

c. 43 × 21; 1930. (See also 544, 549, 600)

538 Carving in the main porch of St Mary's, Liss, Hants, below a figure of the Christ Child: IN GLORIAM DEI MEMORIAM QUE SARAH GABBATT MATRIS DILECTISSIMAE FILIA FILIUSQUE HANC PORTICUM EXSTRANDUM CURAVERUNT MCMXXX. Architect, Sir Edward Maufe.

1930–31. (See also 538A)

538A Tablet on a triple gravestone, on north side of the churchyard, St Mary, Liss, Hants, in memory of SARAH GABBATT, d. 1929.

This is the left-hand tablet of three, the centre one of which is surmounted by a cross, the base of which is inscribed with a chi-rho, 1930.

538B Hopton-Wood tablet, on a black marble background, at Sennicotts Church, Hants, in memory of ELIZABETH TEASDALE, 1825–1913, CHRISTOPHER TEASDALE 1853–1934 and EMILY his wife, 1850–1929.

Caps and lower case, centred, the names in red.

30 × 26; c. 1930.

539 Tall cross, with the shaft inscribed in caps in memory of LOUISA ANNIE GRAY, 1860–1929.

c. 1930.

540 Signboard of painted letters: TAXIDERMIST, made for exhibition purposes for the Department of Circulation, Victoria & Albert Museum, London.

Presumably this word was chosen so as to include an 'X', two 'T's, 'I's and six other different letters.

15 × 90; 1930.

541 Hopton-Wood stone wall tablet on the north wall of St James's, Piccadilly, London, S.W.1, in memory of MARY BEATRICE JOHNSON, 1857–1929.

Five caps of lower case, red and black, the last line in italic. The 'M's differ, also the angles of the 'A's; the 'Y's have pointed ends.

18 × 22; 1930.

542 Hopton-Wood stone tablet in Rycote Chapel, Thame, Oxon., in memory of ALFRED ST GEORGE HAMERSLEY, K.C., J.P., M.P. 1910–1918, 'Who lived at Rycote 1911–1929 and preserved this chapel'.

Now an Ancient Monument. At Miss C. Hamersley's request the tablet, unusually, was signed by E.G.

13 × 30; 1930.

543 Brass tablet with inscription and coat of arms, St Mary, Pyrton, Watlington, Oxon., in memory of ALFRED ST GEORGE HAMERSLEY, 1848–1929.

Thirteen lines caps and lower case well 'condensed' where the text required. The shield bears three rams' heads and the crest, a gold eagle holding a crosslet fitchee.
28 × 30; 1930. (See also 542)

544 Ledger of York stone, in the private graveyard, St Michael and All Angels, Himley, Staffs., in memory of GEORGINA, Countess of DUDLEY, 1846–1929.

Grand 3 in. caps in seven lines centred.
c. 40 × 20; 1930.

545 Tablet in the ante-chapel, New College, Oxford, in memory of German Nationals, men of the College, who fought and died for their country, 1914–1918: PRINZ WOLRAD-FRIEDRICH ZU WALDECK-PYRMOUNT; FREIHERR WILHELM VON SELL; ERWIN BEIT VON SPEYER.

Five lines of caps. Architects, Adams, Holden & Pearson.
R 13 × 58; 1930. (See also 398)

546 Ledgerstone in the churchyard, St James, Bushey, Herts., in memory of JOHN SAXON MILLS, M.A., Barrister-at-Law, d.1929.

Caps followed by an inscription in Greek: ΤΟΔΕΧΑΡΙΣ ΜΑΤΟΥΘΕΟ ΥΖΩΗΑΙΩΝ ΙΟΣ.
41 × 18; 1930. (See also 604)

547 Inscriptions, incised and gilded, in St George's Chapel, Windsor, on the black marble bases of tall bronze candlesticks in the chancel, recording the gift by King George V and Queen Mary in memory of KING EDWARD VII and QUEEN ALEXANDRA.

R 2 × 21 and 4 × 11; 1930.

548 Headstone (wrongly said in the Inventory to be at Clovelly, Devon), the inscription with three shields surmounted by a carving of Christ the King, with his Mother and St Mary Magdalen, in memory of SIBELL MARGARET LUMLEY, 1855–1929, married 1874 Victor Alexander, Earl Grosvenor; secondly, George Wyndham, M.P. She died at Saighton Grange, Cheshire, 1929.

A wonderful drawing of 1930 shows a memorial 5 ft 4 in. high by 10 ft 4 in. with grand 4 in. caps of great character with joined and 'nesting' letters. Lady Grosvenor's grave is in fact at Bruera, near Saighton, and would not appear to be by E.G. A low-walled enclosure has a crucifix above, a bas-relief of a pelican, and five shields.

548A/P Numerals for a clock commissioned by Mr E. W. Hunter, Chairman and founder of the Sun Engraving Co., with monograms of E.W.H.

The case designed by E.G. is painted in a soft green; the bronze clock dial has a genial face in spectacles with sun and moon in lighter coloured metal. Shown in the Arts Council's 'Thirties' exhibition, 1985. c.1930.

549 Ledger of York stone in the private memorial garden, St Michael and All Angels, Himley, Staffs., in memory of ROSEMARY MILLICENT, VISCOUNTESS EDNAM, 1893–1930.

Large caps – and 'Viscountess' cunningly shortened, to fit 'Millicent' by a composite letter, 'VNT', and the 'ESS' smaller.
R 42 × 20; 1930. (See also 537)

550 Tablets of Hopton-Wood stone in the hall of the former Fairbairn House, 310 Barking Road, Plaistow, London, E.13, now the Mansfield Centre, commemorating the gift of the first Fairbairn House opened in 1900 as the Boys' Club of Mansfield House University Settlement.

> The wide central tablet about 6 ft × 2 ft has four lines of 3 in. caps, the first and last widely spaced – 'This house is built to the glory of God and for the inspiration, enjoyment and delight of the boys of London. DESIDERIO PULCHRIORIO.' The side panels, about 2 ft square, have a texture of lower case and italic, about ten lines each. Architects, Louis de Soissons & Grey Wornum.
> R 15 × 6 and 18 × 20; 1931.

551 Hopton-Wood stone tablet, the inscription in caps surmounted by dolphins, at 9 Montpelier Crescent, Brighton, recording 'FREDERICK WILLIAM ROBERTSON – "Robertson of Brighton", Preacher and philosopher lived here: 1847–1850.'

> Now largely covered by a panel of poor lettering.
> R 19 × 24; 1930.

552 Tablet of Hopton-Wood stone in St Mary's, Leigh Woods, Bristol, in memory of Canon JOHN GAMBLE, 1859–1929, 'who by his piety and learning enriched and comforted the souls of his people.'

> Lower case centred, within a pilastered frame.
> R 30 × 17; 1930.

553 Incised caps and lower-case letters on Hopton-Wood stone, now broken: VOX DILECTI MEI ECCE ISTE VENIT / The voice of my beloved, behold he comes leaping / SALIENS IN MONTIBUS TRANSILIENS COLLES / upon the mountains and skipping upon the hills.

> R 7 × 36; 1930.

554 Brass plate showing a quartered coat of arms on a lozenge and inscription in memory of ANN, daughter of Sir Richard FANSHAWE, Secretary of War to the Prince of Wales, afterwards King Charles II, who died at Tankersley Park, Barnsley, Yorks., 22 July 1654. Location unknown.

> R 6 × 9; c.1930.

555 Oval tablet of Hopton-Wood stone, apparently intended for St Michael and All Angels, Tenbury Wells, Worcs., in memory of SIR BENJAMIN BROWNE and ANNIE his wife.

> 'Be mindful, O Lord, of thy servants who are gone before us in the sign of faith and rest in the sleep of peace ...' 'Here they were married Feb 9 1861, here they worshipd (sic) for many years and here they gave thanks for their golden wedding.'
> R 36 × 30; 1931.

556 Tall cross with a small crucifix of Portland stone in the private cemetery, St

George's Retreat, Burgess Hill, Sussex, in memory of ROMOLA MARY TRENCH, 1895–1930.

> Inscription in Italian.
> R 16 × 8; 1931.

557 Hopton-Wood stone tablet in the library of the Royal Automobile Club, Pall Mall, London, in memory of GEORGE CHARLES ASHTON-JONSON, Hon. Librarian of the Club.

> Five lines of caps.
> R 9 × 12; 1931.

557A Inscription: ECCE ABSORBEBIT / FLVVIVM ET NON / MIRABITUR ET HA / BET FIDUCIAM QUOD / INFLUAT / JORDANI SINOFIUS /. Interspersed with the translation in lower case, 'Behold I will drink …'

> The stone has cracked down the lines of certain vertical strokes. The layout is somewhat informal, incorporating small 'nesting' letters in QUOD, for good spacing, and one line composed of caps and the translation together.
> c.24 × 24; 1931.

558 Three-sided obelisk of Clipsham stone, about 7-ft high, topped with a sculptured flame, west of Grove Buildings, Merton College, Oxford in memory of ANDREW COMYN IRVINE, 1902–1924, who 'perished near the summit of Mount Everest, June 1924'.

> Eleven lines of caps, centred. 1931.

559 Inscription on Portland stone (apparently intended for the Lych Gate, Westdean, Seaford, Sussex) with two bas-reliefs in memory of EVELYN JAMES.

> R 16 × 81; 1931.

560 Ledger of grey granite with a cross in the private Royal graveyard at Frogmore, Windsor, in memory of LOUISE MARGARET ALEXANDRA VICTORIA AGNES (third daughter of H.R.H. Prince Frederick of Prussia) 1860–1917, Duchess of Connaught and Strathearn.

> This large memorial solved the problem of a long inscription in a typically logical way by distributing the seventy words in two lines on all four sides. On the upstand of the upper stone, with a cross in relief, in 4 in. caps: BLESSED ARE THE DEAD WHICH DIE IN THE LORD / THEIR WORKS / DO FOLLOW THEM: HER NAME WAS BELOVED / IN MANY LANDS.

> Unique among E.G.'s ledger slabs, the nature of the memorial and the choice of grey granite was probably a requirement of the commission. The 'V'-cut lettering, possibly painted initially, is now weathered and alas virtually illegible. (The date of the stone reflects the fact that the original burial in 1917 was in St George's Chapel, Windsor, and reburial took place in the private Royal burial ground at Frogmore.)
> 10 ft × 5 ft 6 in. – 3 ft 8 in. 1931.

561 Gravestone in York stone, in memory of RICHARD HENRY MORTEN, 1858–1930, of Hill's House, Denham, Bucks., 'His neighbour's friend'.

> Ten lines of caps centred.
> R 23 × 19; 1931.

562 Brass tablet with an incised figure of a bishop, in St Mary's, Bourne St, London, in memory of Bishop JOHN BIDWELL, C.B.E., D.D., 1872–1930.

> c.4 ft high; 1931.

562A Tablet of Portland stone in Jesus College Chapel, Cambridge, with a Latin inscription in memory of HENRY ARTHUR MORGAN.

> R 12 × 45; 1931. (See also 278)

563 Plaque at Brownhill House, Great Brickhill, Bucks., CHARLES WHIBLEY LIVED IN THIS HOUSE ...

> Architect, Detmar Blow. Four lines of 2 in. caps.
> R 14 × 30; 1931.

564 Brass plate in memory of CHARLOTTE, Lady ROBERTSON, C.B.E., d.1931, wife of Sir Benjamin Robertson, K.C.S.I., K.C.M.G., C.I.E.

> R 29 × 19; 1932.

565 Brass tablet at St Nicholas, Brushford, Dulverton, Somerset, in memory of ELISABETH CATHARINE HOWARD, daughter of Henry and Charlotte Howard of Greystoke, wife of Henry, 4th Earl of Caernarvon, 1856–1929.

> Fourteen lines, lower case and italic at the foot – 'Lovers of God and every one that loveth is born of God & knoweth God ... In sua voluntate ...'
> R 23 × 12; 1931. (See also 519)

566 Hopton-Wood stone tablet for a room in a house in Hampstead built by American and Scottish friends of JAMES RAMSAY MacDONALD, in gratitude for his visit to America as Prime Minister, in 1929.

> 9 × 17; 1931.

567 Headstone about 4-ft high at Wollaton, Notts., in memory of Lt.-Col. DUDLEY PERRY FORMAN, 1888–1930, who died as a result of a riding accident: 'his neighbour's friend'.

> 1931.

568 Round-headed Portland gravestone with crossed keys within a roundel in Chichester Cemetery with inscriptions on both sides. Front: In memory of HENRY HOLDING MOORE, 44 years Sacristan of Chichester Cathedral, 1839–1911, and of his wife JESSY MITCHELL MADDOCKS, 1833–1911. Back: In memory of their children, CECIL EDWARD, 1876–1895 & ARTHUR GORDON WENSKY, 1886–1912. Also of JESSY LILLIAN AND LILY & GILBERT DIXON, who died in infancy.

> (H. H. Moore was E.G.'s father-in-law.)
> R 44 × 21; 1931. (See also 422)

568A/P Similar inscriptions on four sides of a stone bird bath at Pigotts.

> Caps, lower case and italic.
> c. 24 × 12 × 12; c.1931.

569 Portland headstone in Chiswick Cemetery in memory of GASPAR ROBERT
KING, 1829–1910 and of his wife ROSE, 1833–1891 (E.G.'s maternal grandparents).
Also in memory of their daughter ELIZABETH, 1860–1926.

> Twelve lines of caps. 1932.

570 Portland headstone in memory of HENRY NICHOLAS MIDDLETON, 1845–1928
and his wife SOPHIA ELIZABETH 1848–1927.

> The drawing shows a coat of arms with a crest 17 in. high and a figure of Isaiah.
> R 16 × 16; 1931.

571 Oak tablet, in caps incised and gilded, in the Record Room, Oxford University
Press: 'This room formerly the office of the Bible printers of the University, has
been furnished as the Record Room of the printing house by the gift of
Constance Meade, great granddaughter of Bishop Percy of Dromore, who in his
own day contributed to the learning of this Press.'

> R 9 × 52; 1931.

572 Panel in the entrance hall, Broadcasting House, London, recording: 'Architect,
GEORGE VAL MYER; Partner, F. J. WATSON-HART; Civil Engineer,
M. T. TUDSBERY; Sculptor, ERIC GILL; Clerk of Wks, G. R. BRITCHFORD; Master
Bldr, W. HASSELDINE; Foreman, E. STAPLER – 1931.'

> (See also 577 for inscription in bronze letters in the entrance hall.)

*572A/P Coat of arms of Rt Revd L. J. White-Thomson, Bishop of Ely, in Bath stone,
with motto DEUS PROVIDEBIT over, on the Morley Horder Building, Jesus
College, Cambridge.

> The shield impaling the three crowns of the bishopric of Ely are borne by two fine
> angels, one holding the mitre above the shield: high relief and vigorous silhouette.
> Architect, Morley Horder.
> c. 7 ft × 12 ft; 1931.

573 Ledgerstone of Portland stone in memory of EDITH NETTLESHIP, 1871–1931.

> Ten lines of 3 in. caps.
> R 65 × 26; 1931.

574 Headstone of Cornish slate in St Nun's, Pelynt, Looe, Cornwall, in memory of
WILLIAM SHUCKFORTH GRIGSON, Priest, 1845–1930.

> c. 1931.

574A Inscription incised in stone for mantelpiece in 'Elmstead', West Wittering,
Sussex, the house then occupied by Sir Henry Royce. QUIDVIS RECTE FACTUM
QUAMVIS HUMILE PRAECLARUM.

> As recorded by Lt.–Col. L. F. R. Fell, in the *Guardian*, 27 March 1963, commemorating the
> centenary of Sir Henry Royce: 'Gill was staying with his father, the Vicar of West
> Wittering. Royce became friendly with Gill, and they often met. At one of their meetings
> Gill asked Royce what he thought was the basic reason for his success. Royce replied,
> "I have always believed that whatever I do, however humble the job is, if I do it as well as

52   Eric Gill's drawing for the Middleton grave, 1931 (570).

53   Coat of arms at Jesus College, Cambridge, 1931 (572A/P).

I can, it is noble." Gill was so pleased with this thought that he had the words freely translated into Latin, and presented Royce with the inscription carved over his fireplace.' c.1931. (See also 644)

*575 Portland tombstone surmounted by a reigning crucifix and figures of the two Marys and St John, together with footstone, in Canford Cemetery, Bristol, in memory of ABIGAIL PHILOMENA CHUTE, 1855–1931. 'Fortuna beata pacifici.'

It has a distinguished base, composed of linked arches in low relief. 1931.

576 Portland head- and footstone in Canford Cemetery, Bristol, in memory of DESMOND MACREADY CHUTE, 1895–1927.

1931.

576A/P A similar headstone to 576 for ANNIE MARY OATES née Hennessy, 1857–1932 – 'Eternal rest …'.

1932.

577 Four-inch and 5 in. bronze letters extending over 19 ft of the wall in the entrance hall, Broadcasting House, Portland Place, London, W.1: DEO OMNIPOTENTI TEMPLVM HOC ARTIVM ET MVSARVM ANNO DOMINI MCMXXXI …

1931. (See also 572)

577A/P Inscription on a book held by an angel on the west side of Broadcasting House, London: OBSCVLTA.

1931.

577B/P Inscription on the base of the Sower in the hall at Broadcasting House: DEUS INCREMENTUM DAT.

1931.

577C/P Panel in the entrance hall, Broadcasting House, to mark the Royal visit.

1932.

578 Portland headstone, with wide pilasters and a footstone, the latter with inscription in Hebrew characters, in Willesden Jewish Cemetery, London N.W.10, in memory of ANNETTE LEWIS, 1862–1931, wife of Eliot Lewis.

'Her little nameless unremembered acts of kindness and of love' in italic, quoting Wordsworth.
R 17 × 12; and the Hebrew inscription 8 in.; 1932. (See 615A/P)

579 Hopton-Wood stone tablet formerly in the chapel at Pigotts, North Dean, High Wycombe, with inscription in Latin, surmounted by a dove carved by Michael Ritchie: EMITTE SPIRITUM TUUM AT CREABUNTUR ET RENOVABIS FACIEM TERRAE, cut for an exhibition in Venice.

A photograph of it appears as frontispiece to Making and Thinking, by Walter Shewring (London: Hollis & Carter, 1959). 1932.

579A/P A credence shelf for the chapel at Pigotts: SICUT OCULI ANCILLAE IN MANIBUS COMINAE SUAE, in red and black.

c.24 × 9; c.1932.

579B/P Inscription round the holy water stoup for the chapel at Pigotts: PARAVI LVCERNAM.

c.1932.

580 Hopton-Wood tablet in Burford Church, Shropshire, the inscription surmounted by a coat of arms, gilt and enamelled, in memory of SIR CHARLES HAMILTON RUSHOUT, fourth and last Baronet, late Royal Horse Guards, of Burford House, Tenbury Wells, 1868–1931. Buried at Longborough, Glos.

Eight lines of caps centred, the names and dates in red. The quartered shield, enamelled, is canted so as to incorporate easily the two crests; the mantling in black, yellow and blue. 42 × 38; 1932.

581 Head- and footstone, St Lawrence, Besselsleigh, Abingdon, in memory of GERTRUDE MAY WALKER, d.1930. Also of her husband the Revd Dr E.M. WALKER, Rector, 1895–1920 and sometime Provost of Queen's College, Oxford.

Caps and lower case centred within a classical scheme. On the footstone, the initials G.M.W. 54 × 28; 1932.

582 Tablet of Hopton-Wood: Beneath this stone rest the ashes of JULIA MARY PLEISTER, NEE MILLAR, 'Whose life on earth ended on the feast of the Annunciation, 1932.'

Eight lines of caps, centred. 15 × 27; 1933.

582A/P Monogram of E.G. forming the tongue of a crocodile carved in the wall of the former Mond Laboratory on the Old Cavendish site, Free School Lane, Cambridge.

The crocodile is about 6-ft long cut in the carved brickwork: the tongue is about 4 in. Architect, H.C.Hughes. When E.G. was on site, chisel in hand, the late Charles Craske, then an assistant in Hughes's Office, called up to him, 'Mr Gill, would you mind if I came up and watched you carving?' Gill replied, 'No, I don't mind, provided you don't mind me not liking you watching me carving'. 1932.

582B/P Three bricks in the wall of the former Mond Laboratory, Cambridge cut or cast: 'H.C.HUGHES Architect 1932. RATTEE & KETT LTD Builders.'

*583 Altar tomb in Ruislip Churchyard, Middlesex, in memory of ANNIE HALL, O.B.E., 1867–1932 and BENJAMIN JAMES HALL, 1868–1934, and with a Latin inscription within an arch.

An unusual and very distinguished stone with arches along all sides and recessed panels between chunky pilasters: the side panels are wider than those at the ends, and thus give a narrow dimension below the top slab. The top is slightly weathered. c.6 ft × 2 ft wide and 2 ft 3 in. high; 1932.

584 Hopton-Wood ledger in All Saints Churchyard, Iden, Rye, Sussex, in memory of ELIZABETH EMMA BEATRICE, BELOVED WIFE OF ADMIRAL SIR AUBREY SMITH, K.B.E., C.B., M.V.O., 1875–1931.

1932.

584A Tablet of grey Hopton-Wood stone inscribed: IF THOU HAST A LOAF OF BREAD SELL HALF AND BUY THE FLOWERS OF THE NARCISSUS.

R 11 × 30; 1932.

585 Headstone in memory of ELEANOR MAY DERRICK, 1918–1932, daughter of Thomas and Margaret Derrick, at Douai Abbey, Upper Woolhampton, Berks.

30 × 30; 1934.

585A Alphabet with roman capitals, and lower-case letters, and numerals incised and coloured on Hopton-Wood stone, signed E.G., 1932.

Commissioned by Sculpture and Memorials Co., London. (Reproduced in E.G.'s *Autobiography* facing p.136.)

586 Monument in the central court of the Robert Thorner Charity Homes, Regent's Park Road, Shirley, Southampton. On the west: the names of the Trustees in 1932; on the East: (18¼ × 19½) details of the benefaction under the will of ROBERT THORNER, who died 17 July, 1690, and lies buried in Baddesley churchyard.

Twenty-two lines of caps and lower-case, justified to the left.
49 × 20; c.1932.

587 Portland headstone in St Marylebone Cemetery, East Finchley, London, N.2, in memory of ELINOR BEAUFOY MILTON, 1911–1931.

R 20 × 20; 1933.

587A/P Train 'headboard' for the FLYING SCOTSMAN painted in Gill Sans.

E.G. himself painted and fixed the name on the engine; his fee included a trip on the footplate. Others were done for trains such as the NORTHERN BELLE and for names of engines under the corporate identity policy of LNER. This later included a 'logo' of LNER with a curved frame.
c.4-ft wide; 1932.

588 Plaque of Portland stone in the refectory of the House of the Resurrection, Mirfield, Yorks., in memory of Bishop CHARLES GORE, 1853–1932, with a bas-relief of the Paschal Lamb and: SURREXI PRAE AMICITIA CAROLI GORE POSUIT ARCHITECTUS i.e. the gift of the Architect, Sir Hubert Worthington.

c.2 ft diam; 1933.

589 Headstone in Golders Green Cemetery, London, in memory of HENRY OPPENHEIMER, 1859–1932.

R 20 × 16; 1933.

590 Portland head- and footstone in the cemetery at Barton, near Cambridge, in memory of IRENE ROBERTS, 1885–1932.

1933.

54   A rare treatment of a table tomb, Ruislip, Middlesex, 1932 (583).

55   Detail of the Lake District map cut in the wall at the Midland Hotel, Morecambe, 1933 (592B/P).

56   Eric Gill at King's Cross after fixing the nameplate which he painted in Gill Sans for the Flying Scotsman, 1932. The ceremony marked the completion of the letter-standardization for the London and North Eastern Railway.

591 Graveboard at Suhr bei Aarau, Switzerland, in memory of MICHAEL D'OYLY
CARTE. AGED 21 YEARS KILLED NEAR HERE IN AN ACCIDENT ON OCTOBER
23rd 1932. THE SON OF RUPERT AND DOROTHY D'OYLY CARTE OF LONDON.

The design shows animals carved on each end.
c.6 ft long; 1933.

592 Hopton-Wood stone tablet in Eton College chapel in memory of HUGH
MACNAGHTEN who occupied Jourdelay's Place, 1899–1920. Vice-Provost of Eton,
d.1929.

2 ft square; 1933.

*592A/P Inscription and names on a large bas-relief in Hopton-Wood stone at the
Midland Hotel, Morecambe.

Fine 3 in. caps on the frame. 'There is good hope that thou mayest see thy friends' (then
ODY in small caps indicating the origin in Homer's Odyssey) and the figures' names,
'Odysseus' and 'Nausicaa' in Greek caps, curving round beneath characteristic formal
foliage; signed E.G. The caps at the foot have 'A's with an angular cross-bar; the 'Y's are
splayed out in the Greek fashion. (The drawing served as the 'masthead' for the menus
on London Midland and Scottish Railway trains with E.G.'s drawn letters: RESTAURANT
CAR – quoting 'Luncheon 3/6 Dinner 4/6'.) Architect, Oliver Hill. 1933.

*592B/P Place names carved on a decorative map of the Lake District on the wall of
the 'Eric Gill Suite' at the Midland Hotel, Morecambe.

The names, e.g. 'Elterwater', curve round the lakes: 'Barrow-in-Furness' curls round like
a knot. Caps, lower case and italic. Architect, Oliver Hill. 1933.

*592C/P Inscription in 4 in. caps round a ceiling panel over the staircase at the
Midland Hotel, Morecambe. 'And hear old Triton blow his wreathed horn.'

Big caps alternately red and blue; slightly misquoting Wordsworth's 'The world is too
much with us', an interesting choice for a seaside hotel.
c.6 ft diam; 1933.

592D/P Inscription on the Portland stone base of the bronze 'Warwick Vase' on the
Senate House lawn, Cambridge, recording the gift by the Duke of Northumberland as Chancellor in 1842.

Nine lines of caps centred, cut by Laurie Cribb. c.1933.

593 Double headstone, of Portland stone, in memory of ALICE JAMESON, 1899–
1932.

A female nude on either side of which are panels of incised letters. Rejected by the
cemetery authorities, this was at one time on loan to the Tate Gallery; location now
unknown. 1932.

594 Foundation stone for London University on the base of the tower, facing Malet
Street, London, W.C.1, laid by King George V, 26th June 1933, 'Her Majesty Queen
Mary being present on the occasion'.

Six lines of caps, centred. Architect, Charles Holden. 1933.

594A/P Inscription carved on the wall near the London University tower, 'Tower: Dry riser' relating to the fire-fighting installation.

1933.

595 Headstone of Hopton-Wood stone (said to have been for Princes Risborough churchyard, Bucks.) in memory of HARRY STALLWOOD, 1897–1933.

R 26 × 18; 1933.

596 Tablet of Roman stone on the circular stair at Heal & Son, Tottenham Court Road, London, W.C.1, recording the Heads of the Business, from 1810.

Caps justified to the left. (From 1959 cut by another hand to match.) The tablet is curved to suit the staircase. Architect, Sir Edward Maufe, succeeding Smith & Brewer. 1933.

597 Wooden tablet in memory of JAMES STEWART MONCREIFF PAUL, 1908–1932.

1933.

598 Portland headstone at Nagpur, Madhya Pradesh, India, in memory of THOMAS VERNON SHUCKFORTH GRIGSON, infant son of W. V. Grigson, Deputy Commissioner of Nagpur, and Phyllis Grigson.

R 43 × 13; 1934.

599 Portland ledgerstone in memory of Brigadier General CHARLES PEARS FENDALL, C.B., C.M.G., D.S.O., 1860–1933.

R 55 × 28; 1934.

600 York ledgerstone in the private graveyard at St Michael and All Angels, Himley, Staffs., in memory of WILLIAM HUMBLE WARD, 2nd Earl of Dudley, 1867–1932.

Nine lines of large caps centred. Distinguished and simple.
R 42 × 21; 1933. (See also 537, 544, 549)

601 Hopton-Wood stone tablet (inscription in Latin) in the War Memorial Chapel, Rossall School, Fleetwood, Lancs., in memory of HERBERT ARMITAGE JAMES, D.D., d.1931.

R 18 × 28; 1931.

602 Portland headstone at Little Hampden, Bucks., of MARY BERNADETTE NUTTGENS, d. February 1926.

Six lines of caps on a simple, small and very distinguished stone, round-headed, moulded simply on the edge.
24 × 15; 1933. (See also 691A)

602A/P Wall tablet in Little Hampden Church, Bucks., commemorating the construction of the vestry, and to the memory of Capt. C. E. A. TREVOR-BATTYE, Lord of the Manor and Churchwarden.

Ten lines of lower case, centred.
c.24 × 20; c.1932.

603 Portland headstone in memory of EDITH T. E. HUELIN, 1857–1933. Stated in the *Inventory* to have been at Speen, Bucks.

> R 27 × 12; 1933.

604 Ledgerstone of York stone at St James the Apostle, Bushey, Herts., in memory of WILLIAM HASLAM MILLS, Barrister-at-Law, 1874–1930 – 'Though the darkness hide thee'.

> Two inch caps. 37 × 17; 1933. (See also 546)

605 Hopton-Wood tablet in the cloisters of New College, Oxford (the inscription in Latin) in memory of GILBERT CHARLES BOURNE, 1861–1933.

> R 26 × 34; 1933. (See also 629)

605A/P Tablet of Hopton-Wood stone with a four-line quotation in italic. Manibus date lilia plenis – Purpureos spargam flores animamque nepotis Bis saltem accumulem donis et fungar inani – Munere.

> Illustration in *Graveyard Memorials in stone and wood*, O.U.P. 1934 – the Report of a Special Committee of the British Institute of Industrial Art. c.1933.

606 Ledgerstone in Wimbledon Cemetery in memory of DAVID BURNS, 1854–1932.

> c.38 × 14; 1933. (See also 655)

607 Cross of Portland stone with a reigning crucifix at the top of the shaft in the churchyard, St Wilfrid's, Burnsall, Skipton-in-Craven, Yorks., in memory of HENRY PHILIP DAWSON of Hartlington, 1850–1933, and of his wife MARY LOUISA, 1850–1932. 'Eternal rest grant unto them, O Lord.'

> An exceptional design, the cross shaft and arms carefully tapered; and with eighteen lines of caps on the face, and Greek on the back horizontally and vertically: Ο ΕΜΟΣ ΕΡΩΣ ΕΣΤΑΥΡΩΤΑΙ.
> R 37 × 20; 1934.

608 The letters RADCLIFFE LIBRARY, c.4 in. high, on the lintel over the main door, together with three coats of arms, on the Radcliffe Science Library, South Parks Road, Oxford. Architect, Sir Hubert Worthington.

> 1933.

608A/P Oak doors in the Radcliffe Library, Oxford, with bas-reliefs and initials of Roger Bacon, William Harvey, Robert Boyle, Sir Christopher Wren, Robert Hooke, and J.J.Dilenius. Architect, Sir Hubert Worthington.

> Chunky caps in oak. 1933.

609 Garden seat of Portland stone in Victor Gollancz's garden at Brimpton, near Reading, in memory of HAROLD REDFERN, the gardener, with an inscription on the front panel: R & V. G. HVNC HORTVLVM FECEBUNT PIGNUS AMORIS; below this, the Hebrew word 'Shalom' – Peace; and on the side: Harold Redfern, gardener.

In his *Reminiscences of Affection* Victor Gollancz tells how E.G., being ignorant of the shape of Hebrew characters, cut the letters 'so spidery that you could hardly see them ... The seat anyhow looked like a tombstone, and we were quite happy to leave it behind when we moved.'

R 12 × 23 and 2 × 9; 1934.

610 Memorial in Jerusalem of Bethlehem stone, in memory of KATRINA, first Lady Conway of Allington, Kent, d.1933.

> R 26 × 25; 1934.

*611 Headstone of Portland stone in Overleigh New Cemetery, Handbridge, Chester, with a coat of arms, and surmounted by a high-relief sculpture of St Francis, in memory of FREDERICK COPLESTONE, C.B.E., J.P. of Chester. Also commemorated are Lt.-Cdr FREDERICK LEWIS COPLESTONE, d.1914 and Commander A. F. COPLESTONE-BOUGHEY, d.1916, both killed on active service.

> The substantial base for the figure is framed with pilasters; the inscription is eleven lines, the shield in low relief.
> R 22 × 23; 1934.

611A/P Inscription on sculpture on the east end of St Thomas's Church, Hanwell, London – a reigning Christ with the B.V.M. and St John holding a book.

> IN PRINCIPIO: AVE REX in raised caps arranged vertically on the cross, divided by the hand of the B.V.M. Architect, Sir Edward Maufe. 1934.

612 Hopton-Wood stone tablet at Clocaenog, Ruthin, N. Wales, inscribed: LORD BAGOT'S PLANTATIONS WERE FELLED DURING AND AFTER THE GREAT WAR 1914–1918. THE FORESTRY COMMISSIONERS BEGAN TO PLANT CLOCAENOG FOREST IN 1930. 1933 R.L. ROBINSON, CHAIRMAN.

> An eight-line inscription with great emphasis on 1930: four lines massed then three justified to the left. Fixed in the base of a big obelisk of rough masonry on a hill-top.
> 36 × 48; 1934.

612A/P Alphabets and numerals, italic with flourished caps, with a monogram of E.G. for the Worshipful Company of Goldsmiths. Designed 'for the benefit of the Silversmith's craft'; engraved by G. T. Friend.

> With a few early letters of the Joanna typeface. 1934.

612B/P Panel of silver, engraved as a sample for a section of an alms dish commissioned by the Worshipful Company of Goldsmiths: IN PRINCI / PIO ERAT / VERBVM.

> This has adjoining panels showing a crucifix and a reigning Christ within typical E.G. foliage. The letters are massed to fill the space and the 'R's, unusually, with curved feet, c.1934. (See 612C/P)

612C/P Silver alms dish, developed from the sample, 612B/P.

> To the original panel (the legs of the 'R' more normal for E.G.) are added ET VERBVM / ERAT APVD (the 'V' and 'D' combined) DEVM, and ET DEVS ER / AT VERBV / HOC ER and AT IN PRIN / CIPIO AP / VD DEVM (the 'V' and 'M' combined and smaller). The extra figurative panels show Adam and Eve and the B.V.M. c.1934.

ABCDEFGHIJKLMN
OPQRSTUVWXYZ
&abcdefghijklmnopqr
stuvwxyz,1234567890

AaBbCcDdEeFfGgHhIiJj
RkLlMmNnOoPpQuqRr
SsTtUVWwvXxYyZz

AaBbCc AaBbCcDdEeFfGgHh

This Plaque of engraved lettering and numerals was designed by Eric Gill for the Worshipful Company of Goldsmiths for the benefit of the Silversmiths' craft in the year 1934. Engraved by G.T. Friend.

57 An alphabet 'for the benefit of the silversmith's craft', 1934 (612A/P).

58   *A silver alms dish commissioned by the Worshipful Company of Goldsmiths, c.1934 (612C/P).*

613 Portland headstone in churchyard of St John the Evangelist, Tolpuddle, Dorset, in memory of JAMES HAMMETT TOLPUDDLE MARTYR PIONEER OF TRADES UNIONISM CHAMPION OF FREEDOM BORN 11 DECEMBER 1811 DIED 21 NOVEMBER 1891.

> A wreath of chain-links within the arched top.
> R 31 × 29; 1934.

614 Hopton-Wood stone tablet with an engraved crucifix on the coffin of DAVID PEPLER, 1906–1934, buried in the churchyard, St Margaret's, Ditchling.

> R 24 × 8; 1934.

615 Hopton-Wood stone tablet at Sevenoaks School, Kent: THIS ASSEMBLY HALL WAS GIVEN TO THE SCHOOL BY CHARLES PLUMPTRE JOHNSON CHAIRMAN OF THE GOVERNORS JUNE 1934.

> R 9 × 18; 1934.

615A/P Portland headstone with wide pilasters and a footstone, the latter with Hebrew characters, in Willesden Jewish Cemetery, London N.W.10, in memory of ELIOT LEWIS, d.1934 aged 80.

> Italic at the foot, 'Guide, philosopher and friend'. This stone makes a charming and restrained pair with that of his wife's (518), like twin beds.
> c.3 ft high; 1934.

616 Portland headstone in Canford Cemetery, Bristol, in memory of BERTRAM HUGHES RIDLER, 1865–1934 – 'He liveth with God'.

> He was the father of Vivian Ridler, Printer to the University of Oxford 1958–1978. 1934.

617 Portland stone cross, surmounted by a crucifix, itself on a bold cross in relief, in St Mary's Cemetery, Kensal Green, London, in memory of ETHEL PES DI VILLA-MARINA, d. 14 October 1933.

> A very bold design slightly tapered, and the lettering in six lines of caps very simply done.
> R 14 × 11; 1935.

618 Portland headstone, surmounted by head and wings of a cherub, in memory of MARTIN JAMES, died 1933 aged 4.

> Caps interestingly arranged – QVI IN PVLCHRI / TVDINE ET INNO / CENTIA DEO / ANIMAM RED / DIDIT.
> R 27 × 13; 1934.

619 Hopton-Wood headstone: MEMENTO / MEI / E.G. / LAPIDARII / MCMXXXVI / HEU MIHI.

> Cut for the Design and Industries Association Exhibition, at the former Dorland Hall, Haymarket, London. In this 'memorial' E.G. anticipated his own death by four years. It is referred to in a letter to Graham Carey, in *Letters of Eric Gill*, p.409.
> R 21 × 15; 1934. (See also 762)

620 Portland rectangular headstone: REMEMBER PHILOMEL, 1845–1923. ATE WORMS SANG SONGS R.I.P.

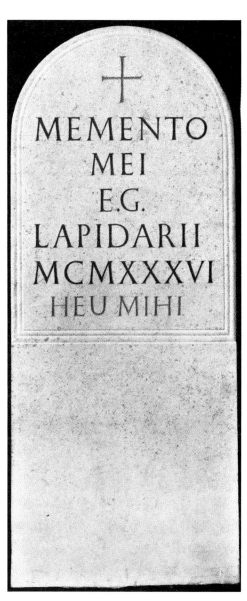

59 *A textured base of lettering for a high-relief sculptured memorial,*
Chester, 1934 (611).

60 *Eric Gill's premature gravestone for exhibition in*
London, 1934 (619).

Cut for the Design and Industries Exhibition (as 619). (On the reverse of the sketch is an alternative inscription: PRAY FOR ME / PHILOMEL / Summer & Winter / as I lie with the / roof so near the / floor … / 1882–1936 / R.I.P.)

R 24 × 19; 1934.

621 Panel for the D.I.A. Exhibition (as 619) incorporating drawings of figures and various kinds of lettering and shorthand.

1934.

622 Gravestone in the cemetery adjoining the School Chapel, Douai Abbey, Upper Woolhampton, nr Reading, in memory of OLIVIA FANNY WHITE, 1841–1933, Lady of the Manor of Bucklebury.

1934.

623 Portland headstone in memory of OLIVE BEATRICE BOCQUET, 1884–1932.

R 12 × 26; 1934.

624 Hopton-Wood headstone in memory of HENRY COTTERILL TILLARD, M.A., 1859–1934, of Cargilfield School, Edinburgh. 'To live in the memory of those who love is not to die.'

40 × 27. 1934.

625 Brass plate set within a Hopton-Wood stone frame, St Peter and St Paul, Great Missenden, Bucks., in memory of Revd HENRY BADHAM, Vicar 1925–34, (not Ernest Robert Lindley, as in the Inventory).

Eight lines (four in italic) and very fine engraved sprays of leaves at the base. c.1935. (cf 648 for the Lindley reference)

626 Portland ledgerstone raised on piers, St Lawrence, Bourton-on-the-Hill, Glos., in memory of DIXON HENRY DAVIES, 1859–1934.

The inscription is on the edges of the stone; a low relief cross on top.

R 29 and 71; 1935.

626A/P Lettering on a sculptured panel DOMINE UT VIDEAM over a door at the Moorfields Hospital Extension, City Road, London.

c.1935.

627 Hopton-Wood stone tablet in Latin in south transept, Merton College Chapel, Oxford, in memory of WALTER WYBERGH HOW, d.1932.

Seven lines of caps, red and black, largely justified to the left; one line of italic with a well-spread 'Q'.

15 × 25; 1935.

628 Portland headstone in memory of HENRY ALBERT SAUL, F.R.I.B.A., 1869–1933.

The stone has a recessed angular panel as for Orpen (634).

R 17 × 15; 1935.

629 Gravestone in the churchyard St Andrew, Sandford-on-Thames, in memory of GILBERT CHARLES BOURNE, D.Sc., F.R.S., 1861–1933.

c.1934. (See also 605)

An inscription, in memory of Constance M. G. Bourne, was added, c.1954.

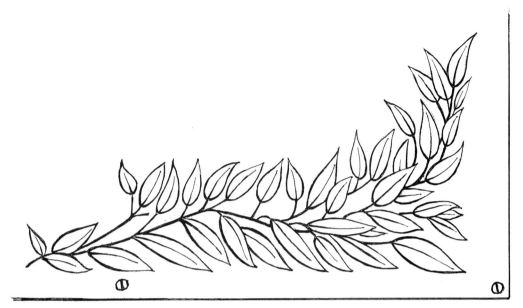

61   Detail of engraved foliage on a brass memorial, St Peter and St Paul, Great Missenden, Bucks., c.1935 (625).

Α Β Γ Δ Ε Ζ Η

Θ Κ Μ Ν Ξ Π Ρ

Σ Τ Υ Χ Ω Φ Ψ

62   Eric Gill's sample Greek alphabet; lamda served by the alpha and omicron by the theta, 1936.

630 Mural tablet of Green Hornton stone in the cloisters, New College, Oxford, in memory of JOHN GALSWORTHY, O.M., 1867–1933.

Six lines of caps, centred.
11 × 23; 1935.

631 Foundation stone of Portland stone for the Guildhall, Kingston upon Thames.

Architect, Maurice Webb. 1935.

631A/P Guildhall, Kingston upon Thames, stone commemorating the opening by H.R.H. Princess Alice, Countess of Athlone, 1935.

631B/P 'Courts & Offices' over door at the Guildhall, Kingston upon Thames, 1935.

632 Recumbent gravestone of Portland stone, All Saints, Sutton, Beds., with the lower part of the inscription in Hebrew, in memory of GEORGE HERBERT BOX, Priest, M.A., D.D., 1869–1933.

74 × 38; 1935.

*633 Stone letters 'BENTALLS' for parapet (proposed to have neon lights) for Bentalls Department Store, Kingston upon Thames, Surrey.

Each letter about 4 ft high, the thick strokes 8 in. wide. This was the first job carved by David Kindersley as an assistant to E.G. There is a coat of arms below in high relief. c.8 ft wide. Architect, Maurice Webb.
c.35 ft wide; 1935.

634 Head- and kerbstones of Portland stone in Putney Vale Cemetery, London, in memory of the artist Sir WILLIAM ORPEN, 1878–1931.

Four lines of caps within the angular recessed panel.
R 18 × 16; 1935.

635 Recumbent gravestone of Delabole slate in St John's churchyard, Hampstead, in memory of the journalist A.R. ORAGE, 1873–1934.

Fifteen lines of spaciously set caps. 'Thou grievest for those that should not be grieved for. The wise grieve neither for the living nor for the dead. Never at any time was I not nor thou, nor these princes of men. Nor shall we ever cease to be hereafter. The unreal has no being. The real never ceaseth to be. A.R. Orage, 1873–1934.' Above is a circle with a pentagram. Sections of the lettering are expanded by small 'V'-cut leaves, serving as punctuation. (See Plate XV in the *Inventory*.)
R 76 × 28; 1935.

636 Monolith of Portland stone, at foot of Headington Hill, Oxford: THIS PARK WAS ACQUIRED BY THE OXFORD PRESERVATION TRUST THROUGH THE LIBERALITY OF THE PILGRIM TRUST AND DAVID AND JOANNA RANDALL-MacIVER. 1932.

Twelve lines, centred 'V'-cut within a recessed panel in the otherwise rough stone. 'OXFORD' and '1932' very large.
12 ft high; 1935.

637 Portland headstone, the inscription surmounted by a coat of arms, in memory of ERNEST JOHN WIGNALL, 1875–1933, Registrar of East London College for forty years. (Not in Manor Park Cemetery as stated in the *Inventory*.)

R 25 × 28; 1935.

637A/P Foundation stone of the Royal Commonwealth Society, Northumberland Avenue, London, W.1: EDWARD / PRINCE OF WALES / LAID THIS STONE IN THE / 26TH YEAR OF THE REIGN OF / KING GEORGE V / 3RD JUNE 1935.

Six lines in two sizes skilfully contrasted, stressing in large caps the Prince of Wales and the King; aligned with two courses of ashlar in the base of the building.
c.36 × 24; 1935.

637B/P Name stone of THE ROYAL COMMONWEALTH SOCIETY, Northumberland Avenue, London, W.1 on the side of the entrance from the foundation stone (637A/P).

1935.

638 Portland ledgerstone at St Mary and St Lawrence, Gt Waltham, Essex, in memory of HUGH WESTERN, 1876–1934, younger son of Lieut.-Col James Halifax Western, C.M.G., R.E., and husband of Mary Theodora Western, 1876–1934. 'The gift of God is eternal life.'

Thirteen widely spaced lines of caps.
R 53 × 28; 1935.

639 Recumbent gravestone, at Monkland Cemetery, Coatbridge, Strathclyde, in memory of ANDREW KIRKWOOD McCOSH, 1841–1916 of Merksworth & Parkhill Dairy, Ayrshire.

R 17 × 38; 1936.

639A York ledgerstone, Monkland Cemetery, Coatbridge, Strathclyde, in memory of JAMES McCOSH, 1872–1903, SARA MACANDREW McCOSH, 1874–1877 and MARY SARA McCOSH, 1882–1883.

R 23 × 26; 1936.

639B Gravestone of York stone, Monkland Cemetery, Coatbridge, Strathclyde, in memory of WILLIAM WADDELL McCOSH, 1883–1935.

R 9 × 35; 1936.

640 Portland head- and footstone at Trumpington Cemetery, Cambridge, in memory of OLIVER PRIOR, 1878–1934, Fellow of St John's College, Cambridge, and first Drapers Professor of French.

Nine lines of caps, with subtle changes of size.
R 37 × 25; and 8 × 6; 1935.

641 Headstone of Hopton-Wood stone in Golders Green Cemetery, London, in memory of NELLIE daughter of Henry and Clara OPPENHEIMER.

With an adapted quotation at the foot in italic, 'She will not grow old …' etc.
1935.

642 Headstone of Hopton-Wood stone with inscription in Pitman's shorthand which reads: In memory of John Smith, 1870–1935, in the beginning was the word.

> Cut for an exhibition of the Arts & Crafts Exhibition Society (now the Society of Designer Craftsmen) in 1936. It was also shown in the French Gallery, November 1936.
> R 24 × 14; 1935. (See also 655A)

642A/P Inscriptions at Talbot Heath School, Bournemouth, on the lunettes over the doors of the Houses: St Mary, St Margaret, and St Catherine. Architect, Sir Hubert Worthington.

> The titles are in caps, arranged vertically, to identify the bas-relief figures. c.1935.

643 Hopton-Wood stone tablet in St James-the-Less, Hadleigh, Suffolk, in memory of FRANCIS EDWARD CARTER, Rector of Hadleigh and Dean of Bocking, 1911–27, d.1935.

> At the foot, in italic 'Remember me, O Lord, according to the favour that thou bearest unto Thy people and visit me with thy salvation'.
> R 11 × 36; 1935.

643A/P A tablet was added below in memory of his widow SIBELLA FANNY CARTER d.1940, with italic at the foot.

> 'Thine eyes shall see the King in his beauty: they shall behold the land that is very far off. Isaiah XXXIII.17.' 1940.

644 Tablet in Hopton-Wood stone: ELMSTEAD; for a house in West Wittering, Chichester.

> R 6 × 20; 1935. (See also 574A)

644A A portrait panel of Lord Rutherford, in the former Mond Laboratory, on the old Cavendish site, Free School Lane, Cambridge, inscribed RUTHERFORD.

> R 20 × 15; 1935.

645 Portland headstone in memory of MARGUERITE MARY HUGGETT, 1897–1934.

> R 30 × 23; 1936.

645A Inscription, letters incised and coloured in red, on the base of a statue of the Immaculate Conception (c.4 ft high) in Ratcliffe College, Leicester: MARIA SINE LABE ORIGINALI CONCEPTA O P N.

> 1936. (See also 645B)

645B Inscription, letters incised and coloured, in red, on the base of a statue of the Sacred Heart (c.4 ft high) in Ratcliffe College, Leicester: MISEREBITUR SECUNDUM MULTITUDINEM MISERATIONUM SUARUM.

> Crowded caps on four lines like a Roman tombstone. 1936. (See also 645A)

646 Hopton-Wood stone tablet inscribed: IN HOC COGNOVIMVS CHARITATEM DEI QVONIAM ILLE ANIMAM SVAM …

Very widely spaced, vertically and horizontally. (Exhibited at the French Gallery, November 1936.)

R 25 × 37; 1936.

647 Small cross and kerbing of Green Horton stone in Putney Vale Cemetery, in memory of DORIS ELISABETH ANSTED, 1878–1935.

The cross, though small, is elegantly tapered.

R 27 × 13; 1936.

648 Portland headstone with kerbing, in memory of ERNEST ROBERT LINDLEY, 1860–1935, and of his wife ADELAIDE, 1858–1935.

Stated in the *Inventory* to be in Northwood churchyard, Middlesex; but there is no trace there.

R 31 × 25; 1936.

649 Headstone in memory of ALBERT STEPHEN O'BRIEN, d.1936.

650 Hopton-Wood stone panel in the MARGARET MACMILLAN House at Wrotham, Sevenoaks, Kent; built by the generosity of Lettice Floyd and opened by H.R.H. the Duchess of York (later H.M. Queen Elizabeth the Queen Mother).

R 15 × 37; 1936.

651 Inscription, surmounted by five coats of arms (coloured), carved direct on the southwest pier, St Mary's, Hackney Wick, London (Eton College Mission), in memory of WILLIAM CARTER, 'sometime Bishop of Zululand, Bishop of Pretoria and Archbishop of Capetown, and first priest in charge of the Eton Mission, Hackney Wick, 1880–1889, 1890–91'.

Twelve lines of large caps, largely justified to the left – the name and dates in red, the rest in blue. Excellent integration with the architecture. 1936. (See also 652)

652 Inscription, surmounted by four coats of arms (coloured), carved direct on the northwest pier, St Mary's, Hackney Wick, London (Eton College Mission) in memory of ST CLAIR DONALDSON, 'sometime Bishop of Salisbury, Archbishop of Brisbane, Vicar of St Mary Eton, Hackney Wick, 1891–1900'.

Largely justified to the left. Ten lines of large caps, the names and dates in red, the rest in blue. 1936.

653 Portland head- and footstones in memory of LESLIE GEORGE WYLDE, 1894–1935. The letters 'A' 'N' 'Z' 'Y' are incised on the footstone.

R 24 × 27; 1936.

654 Headstone at Holy Trinity, Hatton, Warwickshire, in memory of ANNIE ELIZABETH MAYNARD, 1865–1935.

Six lines of large caps on a low headstone with a finely shaped head to the recessed part. On a footstone, A.E.M.

R 21 × 18; 1936.

655 Portland ledgerstone, the inscription in Latin, in Wimbledon Cemetery, in memory of CLARA SWINBURNE BURNS, 1866–1935.

R 73 × 30; 1936. (See also 606)

655A Headstone of Hopton-Wood stone with inscription in Gregg's shorthand which reads: 'In the beginning was the word.' Cut for exhibition at the French Gallery, November 1936.

> R 24 × 14. (See also 642)

656 Portland ledgerstone at Broad Chalke, Wiltshire, in memory of JOHN CHRISTOPHER WOOD, PAINTER, 1901–1930.

> 74 in. long. R 15 × 24; 1936.

657 Portrait tablet of Portland stone set in a surround of Clipsham stone, in memory of Baron ANATOLE VON HÜGEL, 1883–1922, on the wall outside the Museum of Archaeology and Anthropology, Cambridge, of which he was Curator.

> 1936.

658 Tablet of Portland stone in the crypt of St Paul's Cathedral, London, in memory of Admiral of the Fleet CHARLES EDWARD MADDEN, 1st Bt of Kells, Co. Kilkenny, G.C.B., O.M., G.C.V.O., K.C.M.G., D.C.L., Oxon, LL.D., 1862–1935, and a bas-relief coat of arms with supporters.

> The motto, FORTIOR QUI VINCIT on a fine ribbon, certain letters hidden by the folds. The erminois treatment is unusual. The supporters, not being part of the grant, are uncoloured. The arms occupy half the space; the rest is in eight lines of subtly changed letter sizes. c.24 × 30; 1936. (See also 692)

659 Inscription on Hopton-Wood stone: ET ALIAS OVES … exhibited at the French Gallery, November 1936.

> Cut by David Kindersley, c. February 1936.

*660 Bas-relief carving in three large panels, *The Re-creation of Man* (the gift of the UK Government) in the Council Lobby of the Peace Palace, League of Nations, Geneva (now the UN Building). The central panel (c.35 ft long and 7 ft high) depicts the naked figure of a man with inscription: QUID EST HOMO MEMOR ES EJUS? AD IMAGINEM DEI CREAVIT ILLUM. This is followed by the opening lines of *The Wreck of the Deutschland* by Gerard Manley Hopkins: 'Thou mastering me, God, giver of breath and bread. / World's strand, sway of the sea, Lord of the living and dead. / Over again I feel thy finger and find thee.' The left-hand panel contains five naked men running and NOS AUTEM POPULUS EJUS ET OVES PASCUAE EJUS, and on the right CONSTITUISTI EUM SUPER OPERA MANUM TUARUM, and lions, deer and a rabbit, with lightning and clouds.

> The sculpture is well related to the architecture (and to the galleries, from where it is seen in perspective) as also is the lettering related to the spaces created by the sculptures. There are contrasting letter sizes. Much is in 4 in. caps, the lines 8 in. apart; not, as commonly, a texture of lettering, but well-spaced out, to be read. 1937–8.

> On the lintel below, by another hand is carved an olive branch, and in 6 in. caps, gilded, HERE IS A GREAT WORK FOR PEACE IN WHICH ALL CAN PARTICIPATE. THE NATIONS MUST DISARM OR PERISH. BE JUST AND FEAR NOT. Robert Cecil (Viscount Cecil of Chelwood, Life President of the United Nations Association; Nobel Peace Prize 1937).

661 Head- and footstones at St Mary the Virgin, Buckland, Betchworth, Surrey, in memory of MARY BEVAN, 'Daughter of the 3rd Baron Radstock' – 1871–1935.

> With a cherub's head and a leafy outline to the head of the stone. Seven lines of large caps. 1936. (A later inscription of four lines is by another hand.)

662 Tablet of Hopton-Wood stone in the wall of the Monastery, Capel-y-ffin, near Abergavenny, Gwent: REMEMBER CHARLIE STONES FAITHFUL FRIEND & GUARDIAN OF THIS HOUSE 1928–1935.

> R 12 × 19; 1937. (See also 680)

663 Portland headstone in memory of HELEN BOWER 1854–1936 – 'Stay a moment and think of Helen Bower, who thought of others'.

> 1937.

664 Stone tablet commemorating the installation of electric lighting in the chancel of a church, in memory of GEORGE RUDDLE, d.1923 and his wife, NORA CAROLINE, d.1923.

> c.8 × 12; 1936.

665 Hopton-Wood stone tablet, recording names of vicars of St Andrew's, Roker, Sunderland, erected in memory of the Revd WALTER JOHNSON, 4th Vicar, 1929–1935.

> Architect, E.S.Prior.
> R 11 × 23; 1936. (cf 11, 11A/P)

666 Portland headstone in Putney Vale Cemetery, in memory of HAZEL LAVERY, 1886–1935.

> Sir John Lavery's name was added later in a similar manner.
> R 22 × 24; 1936. (cf Sir William Orpen's stone at Putney Vale, 634)

667 Raised ledger with head- and footstones in Tankersley churchyard, Yorks., in memory of HORATIO NELSON RITCHIE, 1882–1936. On the ends: A BELOVED PHYSICIAN, and THE PATH OF DUTY WAS THE WAY TO GLORY.

> c.1936.

668 An alphabet of roman and lower-case letters and numerals, designed by E.G., carved on Hopton-Wood stone by Laurie Cribb for Sculpture and Memorials Co.

> R 28 × 24; 1935.

669 Panel of Green Hornton stone in Witney, Oxon, in memory of D.J.SMITH.

> 1936.

670 Portland headstone in memory of MARION LILIAS HAMILTON-RUSSELL, 1876–1934, wife of Arthur Hamilton-Russell of Neatham Manor, Alton.

> R 33 × 28; 1937.

671 Inscription on Delabole slate, intended for the grave of THOMAS BARNES, 1785–1841, commissioned by The Times Publishing Co. Panels also

commemorate SARAH DUNN, d.1838 & MARY BARNES, d.1852, now held in *The Times* archives.

Rubbings. The inscription for THOMAS BARNES: 19 × 52 & 17 × 52; for SARAH DUNN: 19 × 13; for MARY BARNES: 15 × 13.
1937. (See also 734A)

672 Plaques of de Freyne's limestone, for beds in a hospital, endowed by the Prudential Assurance Co. (location unknown):

(a) THE SARAH LEWIS BED, 1932 (R 6 × 19)

(b) THE WESTON BED, 1936 (R 11 × 19)

(c) THE PRUDENTIAL ASSURANCE Co. Ltd. BED, 1939 (R 6 × 16)

1937.

673 Sundial of Blue Horton stone with semi-recumbent figure of a woman (carved by Anthony Foster) surmounted by an inscription (carved by E.G.): WHEN THE SUN IS NOT SHINING I DO THIS FOR FUN.

Carved for exhibition purposes and sold to a customer in the U.S.A. 1937.

674 Tablet of Portland stone in St Andrew's, Farnham, Surrey, inscribed: TO THE MEMORY OF GEORGE STURT OF THIS TOWN. HE WROTE WITH UNDERSTANDING AND DISTINCTION OF THE WHEELWRIGHTS' CRAFT AND ENGLISH PEASANT LIFE. BORN 1863 – DIED 1927.

Nine lines of caps, the name and date in red. 1937.

675 Gravestone with a crucifix and a figure of Our Lady in Beaconsfield Cemetery, Bucks., in memory of GILBERT KEITH CHESTERTON, 1874–1936.

1937. (And of FRANCES, his wife, 1869–1938, added 1939)

676 Portland headstone in Surbiton Cemetery in memory of MARIAN MOODY, d.1936: 'Everyone that loveth knoweth God.'

The carving by Anthony Foster, 1937. An additional inscription was cut in 1939 for her husband Percival Sadler Moody. A footstone has 'M.M., P.S.M., Servire deo sapere' motto of the Sadler family.

677 Wall tablet, with portrait in relief for the Maharani Hospital, Jagdalpur, Bastar State, Madhya Pradesh, in memory of MAHARANI PRAFULLA KUMARI DEVI, 1910–1936.

(In the *Inventory* as in the possession of Mr E.S. Hyde, Heswall, Cheshire, who commissioned the work.) 1937.

678 Tablet of Hopton-Wood stone at Holkham Church, Norfolk, inscription with a coat of arms, in memory of ALICE EMILY WHITE, 1855–1936, wife of Thomas William Coke, 3rd Earl of Leicester.

A very distinguished monument. The shield is surmounted by a countess's coronet the same width, treated fairly freely, and supported by leafy fronds, as are also the pilasters at the sides. Nine lines of caps, the name in red; two lines of lower case in red at the foot – and a low-relief inscription in caps on the base of the frame.
c.29 × 41; 1937. (See also 678A/P)

678A/P Tablet of Hopton-Wood stone at Holkham Church, Norfolk, in memory of
GEORGINA CAROLINE CAVENDISH, 1852–1937, wife of Thomas William Coke,
2nd Earl of Leicester, K.G.

> A small and distinguished stone. Six lines of caps, the name and date in red, followed by
> a line of italic, 'Her children rise up and call her blessed'.
> c.30 × 15; 1937.

679 Portland headstone in churchyard of St Mary & St Bartholomew, Cranborne,
Dorset, in memory of MICHAEL CHARLES JAMES CECIL, 1918–34.

> (The angels' wings were carved by John Skelton, E.G.'s nephew, his last apprentice.)
> R 16 × 22; 1937.

680 Portland headstone in the graveyard of the church at Capel-y-ffin, Abergavenny:
REMEMBER CHARLIE STONES CARPENTER DIED 1935 R.I.P.

> R 22 × 12; 1937. (See also 662)

680A/P Tablet at Laurence Sheriff School, Rugby, in memory of HENRY VICTOR
WHITEHOUSE, 1889–1904.

> (This was 51 in the Inventory, wrongly dated 'c.1904'.)
> c.1937.

681 Portland ledgerstone, St Barnabas, Bournmoor, County Durham, in memory of
Major-General, the Hon. Sir WILLIAM LAMBTON, K.C.B., C.M.G., D.S.O., 1863–
1936 – 'Glory to God and thanks for every remembrance of him'.

> Sixteen lines of caps, spaciously arranged and centred, the awards and dates each on
> single lines.
> R 64 × 24; 1937.

682 Hopton-Wood stone tablet on west wall in Holy Rood Church, Watford, in
memory of JOSEPH PATRICK KEATING, 1862–1924, Rector for twenty-two years.

> R 17 × 33; 1937.

683 Portland headstone in Hastings Cemetery, in memory of ROBERT ARTHUR
COOMBS, Priest, 1869–1924, and of his wife BERTHA GEORGINA, 1869–1926.

> 42 × 24; 1937.

684 Tablet for the Eye Hospital (Hospital of St John) in Jerusalem, in memory of
GENEVIEVE LADY WATSON, d. 31 Dec 1936, Dame of Grace of the Order of St
John of Jerusalem, widow of Sir Charles Watson, R.E., K.C.M.G.

> c.34 × 45; 1937.

685 Memorial tablet in the Scotch Church, Jerusalem, in memory of the men
of the BLACK WATCH, ROYAL HIGHLANDERS who fell in battle in Palestine,
commissioned by the 1st and 2nd Battalions, 1917–1918.

> 1937.

686 Tablet for the Eye Hospital, Jerusalem, commemorating the life and work of
WILLIAM EDMUND CANT, M.B.E., F.R.C.S., d.1936.

> 1937.

686A/P Lettering on the wall of the Rockefeller Museum in Jerusalem –
GOVERNMENT OF PALESTINE DEPARTMENT OF ANTIQUITIES.

> Large generously spaced caps in two sizes. c.1937.

686B/P Lettering at the Rockefeller Museum in Jerusalem – NO ADMITTANCE,
repeated in Hebrew and Arabic. Also NORTH CLOISTER etc., similarly repeated.

> c.1937.

687 Portland headstone in Wolvercote Cemetery, Oxford, in memory of ELEANOR
CONSTANCE LODGE, D.LITT., C.B.E., 1869–1936, sometime Vice-Principal of Lady
Margaret Hall and Principal of Westfield College, University of London.

> Nine lines of caps spaciously set, justified to the left in five cases; two lines of italic: 'With
> thee is the fountain of life / in thy Light shall we see light.' A distinguished stone set in
> fourteen acres of mediocre designs.
> R 35 × 32; 1937.

688 Painted lettering for the bookshop of John and Edward Bumpus Ltd, Oxford
Street, London, W.1: THERE ARE, IT MAY BE, SO MANY KINDS OF VOICES IN
THE WORLD, AND NONE OF THEM IS WITHOUT SIGNIFICANCE
(1 Corinthians 14.10).

> Painted by Denis Tegetmeier, E.G.'s son-in-law. 1937.

> (When the bookshop was vacated, these boards were acquired by the Monotype
> Corporation.)

689 Tablet of Portland stone in the Dockyard Church, Portsmouth, in memory of
Sir JOHN DONALD KELLY, 1871–1936, Admiral of the Fleet, G.C.B., G.C.V.O.

> Fine caps and lower case.
> R 47 × 24; 1937. (See also 693)

689A Tablet of Delabole slate at St Peter's, Greenham, Wellington, Somerset,
recording a benefaction given by Mary Kelly, the widow of ADMIRAL SIR JOHN
KELLY, July 1937.

> R 10 × 13; 1937. (See also 693)

690 Slate panel over main entrance of Blackfriars, St Giles, Oxford, inscribed: HUNC
CONVENTUM ALTERUM NOVUM EADEM ...

> Six lines of massed caps, justified to the left. The date is in the Latin form – XVIII KAL
> SEPT MCMXXI.
> 12 × 30; 1937.

691 Head- and footstones in churchyard at St Thomas, Chevithorne, Tiverton,
Devon, in memory of MICHAEL LUDOVIC HEATHCOAT AMORY, b.1914, with a
coat of arms, killed while flying June 7th 1936, aged 22.

> Ten lines of caps, ending with 'Like an unbodied joy, whose race has just begun'. 1937.
> (See also 485)

63   Letters 4-ft high for a parapet, Kingston upon Thames, Surrey, 1935 (633).

NO ADMITTANCE

ممنوع الدخول

הכניסה אסורה

64   Three languages at the Rockefeller Museum, Jerusalem, c.1937 (686B/P).

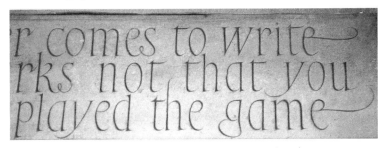

65   Unusual italic for Peek Frean's Sports Pavilion, Lee, Kent, 1939 (736A).

691A/P Portland headstone in Little Hampden, Chorleywood, Bucks.: KATHLEEN MARY NUTTGENS, died Dec. 10 1937 Aged 47 yrs. R.I.P.

> Caps, centred; elegantly restrained. The Nuttgens family were E.G.'s neighbours at Pigotts.

692 Recumbent gravestone of Portland stone, in Chichester Cemetery, in memory of JOHN WILLIAM MADDEN, 1825–1875, Captain Adjutant Royal Sussex Light Infantry and of his son CHARLES EDWARD MADDEN, Admiral of the Fleet, 1862–1935, 1st Bt of Kells, Co. Kilkenny.

> 45 × 94; 1937. (See also 658)

692A Table-stone paperweight with inscription: WHATSOEVER THY HAND FINDETH TO DO DO IT WITH THY MIGHT, cut for Wilma, Lady Cawdor in August 1937.

> (See also 748A)

692B Table-stone (slate) paperweight with inscription: I AM AN AMBASSADOR IN BONDS THAT THEREIN I MAY SPEAK BOLDLY AS I OUGHT TO SPEAK, cut for Wilma, Lady Cawdor as a gift to Charles Morgan.

> 4 × 2; 1937.

*693 Tablet of Portland stone, St Peter's, Greenham, Wellington, Somerset. 'Remember JOHN DONALD KELLY Extra Admiral of the Fleet G.C.B., G.C.V.O' 1871–1936.

> Three lines of caps in red at the top, followed by thirteen lines of raised lower case: 'He served his Sovereign & the Royal Navy faithfully for 52 years & then by the will of God fell asleep Nov 4 1936 aged 65 yrs.' Many appointments are then recorded; and in red italics justified to the left: 'They that go down to the sea in ships … Then are they glad because they are at rest, and so he bringeth them to the haven where they would be.'
> 42 × 25; 1937.

> Below is added a tablet in memory of his wife MARY KELLY 1880–1937. Four lines followed by a line in italic: 'Your joy no man taketh from you.' (Mary was the sister of Lieut. Kelly – see 337 and 344.) c.1937. (See also 689)

693A/P Cross of Portland stone at St Peter's, Greenham, Wellington, Somerset, in memory of MARY KELLY 1880–1937 – caps on the shaft, and at the foot BE STRONG FEAR NOT.

> The shaft (12 in. at the foot) and the arms are tapered in E.G.'s usual way. On the back, eight lines, widely spaced, of caps spanning the shaft, 'Serve the Lord with gladness, come before his presence with a song'. Partly justified to the left, a combined 'TH' and 'BE-FORE' boldly divided.
> 4 ft high; c.1938. (See also 693)

694 Inscriptions, UNIVERSITY PRESS, on each side of the front entrance to the Pitt Building, Trumpington Street, Cambridge.

> 1937.

695 Delabole slate with Hopton-Wood surround in University College, Oxford, in memory of ANDRE JOHN MESNARD MELLY, A.M., M.C., M.A., B.M., Commni. of

the college, 1919–1922. Leader of the British Red Cross Unit in Abyssinia, who died at Addis Ababa, May 5, 1936, aged 37.

R 13 × 20; 1937.

696 Tablet of Delabole slate in the laboratory of the Marie Curie Hospital, Hampstead, recording the equipment of the laboratory in memory of HELEN CHAMBERS, 1879–1935. The hospital was destroyed by enemy action in World War II.

R 11 × 24; 1937.

697 Head- and kerbstones of red Mansfield stone in memory of EDMUND COMMELINE LLOYD, 1888–1936, of Pitsworthy.

24 × 30; 1937.

698 Portland headstone, in memory of FREDERICK WALMSEY HUNTER, 1876–1936. (Site unknown; stated in the *Inventory* as Brent Knoll, Somerset.)

1937.

699 Portland headstone for St Leonard's, Pitcombe, Somerset, in memory of HENRY HOBHOUSE, 1854–1937. (Stated in the *Inventory* to be at Castle Cary.)

1937.

700 Portland headstone in memory of GILLIAN MEROWE CORYTON, 1928–1935.

R 20 × 12; 1937.

700A/P Portland stone crucifix with REGNAVIT A LIGNO DEUS, commissioned by Revd Gerard Irvine.

11 in. high; 1937.

701 Portland gravestone in memory of FRANKLIN JOHN KING, 1855–1936.

R 20 × 12; 1937.

702 Headstone in the churchyard of St Mary the Virgin, Langley Marish, Slough, in memory of WILLIAM FRANCIS NASH, 1931–1935, the son of John and Christine Nash.

c.19 × 20; 1937.

703 Tablet of Delabole slate in memory of FREDERICK HAMLYN, 1846–1904, fixed to the base of a tall wooden crucifix with a pent roof in Clovelly churchyard: 'Generous in spirit, pure in heart, unswerving in justice.'

R 13 × 21; 1937. (See also 68 & 704)

704 Tablet of Delabole slate in memory of CHRISTINE HAMLYN, 1855–1936, wife of Frederick Hamlyn, for fifty-two years devoted owner of Clovelly.

On another face of the base of the crucifix (703).
R 13 × 22; 1937.

704A/P Delabole slate tablet in Clovelly church in memory of CHRISTINE HAMLYN d.1936 within a classical stone surround.

Nine lines of caps, gilt, with some joined letters, below an alabaster inset with a kneeling figure on a cloud between angels. But only the tablet can be attributed to E.G., and perhaps a roundel at the top: ΧΡΙΣΤΟΣ ΑΝΕΣΤΗ.
21 × 12; 1936.

704B/P A kind of headstone with an angular top, formerly at Pigotts, in caps: DEO AUTEM GRATIAS QUI DEDIT NOBIS VICOROAM PER DOMINUM NOSTRUM JESUM CHRISTUM.

Caps 2 in. for DEO and JESUM, 1½ in. for the rest; nine lines, the fifth and sixth justified to the left. Not much room for a long tail to the 'Q' in this case.
17 × 26; c.1937.

705 Tablet in memory of SEYMOUR ASQUITH. Location unknown.

1938.

705A E.G. designed a Portland headstone surmounted by a cross within foliage, for the churchyard at St John the Evangelist, Holdenhurst, Bournemouth, in memory of GERALD GRAHAM PEEL, 1878–1937; but in the event a small granite slab with poor lettering marks the grave.

c.1937. (See also 230)

706 Tablet at Hatfield, Herts., in memory of WILLIAM GASCOYNE-CECIL, D.D., Bishop of Exeter, second son of the 3rd Marquis of Salisbury, K.G.

Included in the Inventory by virtue of a half full-size setting-out, 7 × 39 in., signed by E.G. at Pigotts, 19.1.38. But this does not tally with a memorial tablet in the Lord William Memorial Hall at Hatfield – which cannot safely be attributed to E.G.

706A Alphabet of incised 2 in. letters with numerals.

1938.

707 Headstone of Delabole slate in Bunhill Fields Burial Ground, London, E.C.1, in memory of Revd WILLIAM HOOKE, 1601–1678. 3M.A. Trinity College, Oxford, 1623. Teacher of the First Church in New Haven, Connecticut, 1644–56. Chaplain to Oliver Cromwell & Master of the Savoy Hospital until the close of the Commonwealth.

Thirteen lines, largely justified to the left. In italic at the foot: 'This tablet is erected by the New Haven Church through the generosity of a collateral descendant.' 1938.

*708 Recumbent tombstone of Portland stone, with a coat of arms, in the private graveyard in the parkland of Wilton House, Salisbury, of MICHAEL GEORGE HERBERT, 1891–1932, son of Sir Michael Henry Herbert, P.C., G.C.M.G., C.B.

The dedicatory inscription is well arranged round the vertical face of the stone. The shield, crest and motto ribbon are majestically carved in high relief covering two-thirds of the top of the stone; three lions in low relief on the canted shield. The spiky mantling flows down below the shield and is caught up in the motto ribbon, inscribed: UNG JE SERVIRAY. One of E.G.'s finest heraldic sculptures. 1938.

709 Portland headstone in memory of HENRY DAVID APPERLY, d.1937, at St James's, Gerrard's Cross, Bucks. A footstone, H.D.A., has a later inscription in memory of his wife by another hand.

> 42 × 13; 1938.

709A Head- and footstones of Delabole slate, St Stephen's, Lympne, Hythe, Kent, in memory of A. H. HALLAM MURRAY, artist and publisher, born at 50 Albemarle Street 1854, died 1934.

> Above is a low-relief circle with alpha and omega within weeping willow boughs; the first line bears a circle with a chi-rho also.
> R 24 × 26; 1938. (A later inscription is by another hand.)

709B/P Base of sundial in Portland stone with a bas-relief of birds at Margaret MacMillan House, Deptford, London, S.E., 'This garden was made in 1937 in memory of G. J. B. Turner'.

> Roman caps. c.1938.

709C/P Base of a bird-bath at Margaret MacMillan House, Deptford, cut as for 709B.

709D/P Altar for Blundell's School, designed by E.G. and carved by the boys with bas-reliefs; inscribed above Christ's head on the front, 'This is my body which is given for you'.

> The letters characteristically fill the informal space between the haloes of the disciples, but the letter forms, cut by the boys, are uncharacteristic of E.G. 1938.

710 Lectern in Hopton-Wood stone, in All Saints Church, Lusaka, Zambia, in memory of Lady YOUNG, wife of Sir Hubert Young, inscribed on the column (letters successively beneath one another): IF I TAKE THE WINGS OF THE MORNING, EVEN THERE SHALL THY HAND LEAD ME ...

> 4 ft × 4 ft 5 in.; 1938.

711 An alphabet carved for Mr Grady, an American client of Sculpture and Memorials Co., London.

> 1938.

712 Inscription: PLAYHOUSE, in widely spaced caps above the first-floor windows on the Theatre in Beaumont Street, Oxford. Architect, Sir Edward Maufe.

> 1938.

713 Memorial of Portland stone outside south transept of Peterborough Cathedral, in memory of EMILY JANE STOCKS, 1847–1937 – the inscription on the sides of a form of hogsback, in the form of a Latin cross.

> Adjoining Canon Stocks (517). 1938.

714 Ledgerstone of green Cumberland slate in Cloister Garden, Canterbury Cathedral, in memory of HUGH RICHARD LAWRIE SHEPPARD, 1880–1937. 'These things I command you that ye love one another.'

Widely spaced caps; a stone of great restraint and dignity. 'Dick' Sheppard was Dean of Canterbury, after many years as Vicar of St Martin-in-the-Fields, London.
R 67 × 23; 1938.

715 Cross of Portland stone with a panel below in Ladywell Cemetery, Brockley, London, S.E.4, in memory of ALICE ANN JONES 1856–1937.

The arms of the cross are tapered: centrally, the chi-rho in relief. Ann Jones was the mother of David Jones – whose own memorial is on a circular stone within the kerb.
R 15 × 17; 1938.

716 Hopton-Wood stone tablet in memory of WALTER DOUGLAS WELLS, M.A. Cantab., 1889–1938, for twenty-three years a master at Chigwell School, Essex.

R 9 × 27; 1938.

717 Headstone with kerbing in Aberdeen grey granite stated in the *Inventory* to be at Drumoak, Aberdeen, in memory of Sir ROBERT WILLIAMS, Baronet, 1860–1938.

1938.

717A/P Lettering on a book on a statue of St Thomas More at R.C. School, Newcastle under Lyme, Staffs.

Divided thus across the pages CAES / ARIS:CAES / ARI: ET QU / AE SVNT / DEI DEO; the last word much larger. 1938.

717B/P Lettering on a book on a statue of St John Fisher, similar to 717A/P: TU ES / PETRUS: ET SUP / ER HANC PE / TRAM AEDIFI / CABO ECCLE / SIAM.

1938.

718 Tablet of Delabole slate, formerly in Zion Congregational Church, Coronation Road, Southville, Bristol, in memory of THOMAS SILCOX CLEVERDON, 1866–1937, and JANE LOUISA CLEVERDON, 1871–1937. The parents of Douglas Cleverdon.

Now in Bristol Museum.
R 10 × 13; 1938.

719 Tablet in Hampstead Cemetery in memory of JOHANNA GUTTMANN, 1854–1938.

1938.

720 Grey marble tablet at Stanway, Glos., in memory of MARY CONSTANCE WEMYSS, 1862–1937. Beneath this inscription is a brown sprig of laurel with: VALE PAULISPER DILECTISSIMA.

R 13 × 24; 1938. (See also 733A)

721 Foundation stone of the R.C. Church, St Peter the Apostle, Gorleston-on-Sea, Great Yarmouth.

Carved on three sides of the stone which forms the base of the altar: four lines of caps in Latin. The church, designed by E.G., was consecrated in June 1939. 1938.

721A/P Inscription on the hanging rood at St Peter's, Gorleston, DOMINE ADJUTOR MEUS / ET REDEMPTOR MEUS, arranged crosswise.

> The 'M' in DOMINE and REDEMPTOR serves as the centre of the cross. 1938.

721B/P Inscription above the water tap in the sacristy at St Peter's, Gorleston: DA DOMINE VIRTUTEM.

> 1938.

722 Ledger of York stone, in memory of NICO JUNGMAN, 1872–1935.

> R 18 × 22; 1939.

723 Two oak panels with incised lettering in the Chapel, Rossall School, Fleetwood, Lancs., commemorating the gift by Old Rossallians of windows in memory of LEONARD ROMNEY FURNEAUX, 1859–1934, a master of the school 1884–1920.

> 1938.

724 Portland headstone in Beckenham Cemetery, Kent, in memory of ESSIE. A. HOLMES (sic) 1860–1938.

> The name on two lines justified to the left … the dates centred.
> 30 × 18; 1938.

725 Hopton-Wood stone tablet, now destroyed: ΒΙΤΖΗΛΟΒΡΥΣΙΣ (translation: VITZELOVRUSIS – The spring of Vitzelos) followed by an elegiac couplet.

> Commissioned by John Pendlebury, F.S.A., on which a note appears in the Inventory. A sketch layout survives for the tablet, 21 × 46. 1939.

726 Ledger of Cumberland slate in the crypt of Westminster Cathedral, London, in memory of COUNT ALEXANDER PHILIP CONSTANTINE LUDOVIC BENCKENDORFF, 1849–1917.

> Ten lines of Old Slavonic, a simple shield in the centre, then eleven lines of Latin caps, 1¼ in. In the Russian, the phi is generously wide, with two big lobes; the delta has, like some ancient examples, cockspur serifs on the lowest stroke; the 'γ' is curved at the end, not chopped off. The inscription refers to his being Ambassador and Plenipotentiary Extraordinary from the Russian Empire, the last such in fact. The shield, slightly recessed, bears on a pale three roses.
> R 69 × 23; 1939.

727 Portrait panel of Hopton-Wood stone with pilasters, beneath which is an inscription in nine lines of caps in memory of OTTOLINE MORRELL, 1873–1938, sister of the 6th Duke of Portland.

> This work, formerly in the possession of Lady Ottoline's daughter, is now in St Mary's, Garsington, Oxon.
> R 17 × 21; 1939. (See also 730)

728 Portland headstone in the churchyard, St Botolph's, Farnborough, Banbury, in memory of STANLEY MOTTRAM RANKIN, d. 1933, and of MARY, his wife, d. 1935.

> Eight lines of caps spaciously set out.
> R 31 × 24; 1939.

729 Tablet of Hopton-Wood stone, in St Winifred's Church, Holbeck, Worksop, Notts., in memory of Major Lord WILLIAM AUGUSTUS CAVENDISH-BENTINCK, 1899–1932.

> R 33 × 20; 1939.

729A/P Delabole slate tablet in Clovelly church in memory of Brigadier the Hon. ARTHUR ASQUITH D.S.O., d.1939: 'Known unto God' within a classical surround.

> Seven lines gilt, centred, and probably a safe attribution to E.G. because of other Asquith commissions (see 338, 414, 515 and 705). Arthur Asquith was the third son of the first Earl of Oxford and Asquith. There is a later inscription below for his widow.
> 21 × 11; 1939.

730 Ledgerstone of Hopton-Wood at St Winifred's, Holbeck, Worksop, Notts., in memory of OTTOLINE MORRELL, 1873–1938.

> Four lines of caps. 1939. (See also 727)

731 Stations of the Cross, in Hopton-Wood stone, St Albans, Charles Street, Oxford.

> These are virtually line engravings filled in red, blue and black, the numbers 'V'-cut, simply expressed with letters combined or small, as the length requires for spacing. In the twelfth Station the crucifix has a scroll, held by St John lettered in Greek: ΑΓΑΠΑΤΕΜ.
> 18 × 15; 1939–40.

732 Raised table-stone of Portland stated in the *Inventory* to be in Blakeney Churchyard, Holt, Norfolk, in memory of KENNETH EDGAR MYLNE BARKER. Also of Annabella Catherine, his wife.

> c.72 × 33; 1939.

732A Alphabet on Hopton-Wood stone, the letters of roman caps and lower-case with arabic numerals, incised and coloured.

> Above is a text from Virgil, 'Felix qui potuit' and (at foot) 'rerum cognoscere causas', in italic and 'signed' '1939 E.G.', carved by E.G. for Graham Carey. (See Plate XVI in the *Inventory*.)
> R 22 × 17.

732B An alphabet on Hopton-Wood stone of roman and lower-case letters, together with numerals, incised and coloured. For Sculpture and Memorials Co.

> R 17 × 23; 1939.

732C An alphabet on Hopton-Wood stone of roman and lower-case letters, together with numerals, incised and coloured. For Sculpture and Memorials Co.

> R 23 × 17; 1939.

732D An alphabet on Hopton-Wood stone, of roman and lower-case letters, together with numerals, incised and coloured. For Sculpture and Memorials Co.

> R 18 × 24; 1939.

733 Carving in Portland stone at Lodge Hill Farm, Butler's Cross, Aylesbury, Bucks., the residence of E.A.Randag, depicting St Hubert and stag. This is surmounted by a crucifix and an inscription reading: EGO SUM JESUS QUEM PERSEQUERIS.

In his diary, under 25 Sept., 1940, E.G. records having worked on this carving *in situ* all that afternoon. An entry the following day records having finished it. This appears to have been his last stone carving.

733A Memorial in a form of hogsback (cf 713) of Portland stone with inscriptions on the sides and ends, in the churchyard, Didbrook, Stanway, Glos., in memory of MARY wife of Hugo 11th Earl of Wemyss, 1862–1937. 'For more than 50 years she made Stanway a home beloved by all who came.' On the west end, a shell and 1863–1927; on the east end 'And the greatest of these is Charity'.

    1939. (See also 720)

734 Head- and footstone of Hopton-Wood stone, at Framingham Earl, near Norwich, REMEMBER GEOFFREY COLMAN, 1892–1935.

    Four lines of caps and then five lines of italic.
    R 30 × 21; 1939.

734A Tablet of Delabole slate fixed to the new building at 23–25 Soho Square, London, W.1, commemorating THOMAS BARNES, 1785–1841 (Editor of *The Times* 1817–1841) who lived there.

    R 15 × 25; 1939. (See also 671)

735 Celtic cross of green Hornton stone at Knockdolian, Strathclyde, in memory of HENRY WILSON McCONNELL, M.A., M.B. (Cantab), M.R.C.S. (Eng.).

    R 18 × 7; 1939.

*736A A tablet of Roman stone on Peek Frean & Company's Sports Pavilion, Sidcup Road, Lee, Kent, recording the gift of the pavilion by the President of the Club, Philip Carr.

    Together with 736B, these two tablets contain remarkable changes in letter form: red and black, caps and a very large italic; cheerful touches of detail. A rare and delightful example.
    12 × 51; 1931. (See also 736C)

*736B Tablet at Peek Frean's Pavilion lettered: AND WHEN THE ONE GREAT SCORER COMES TO WRITE AGAINST YOUR NAME – HE MARKS NOT THAT YOU WON OR LOST BUT HOW YOU PLAYED THE GAME. (From *Alumnus Football* by Grantland Rice.)

    One of E.G.'s most remarkable inscriptions, as noted for 736A.
    R 12 × 77; 1939.

736C Clock face at Peek Frean's Pavilion in arabic figures 1 to 12 – some upside down.

    16 in. diam; 1939.

737 Headstone stated in the *Inventory* as in Chelsfield Churchyard, Kent, 'In happiest memory of CHARLES RONALD VAWDREY COUTTS' 1876–1938 'Promptus'.

    The lines of lettering especially distinguished by being widely spaced.
    R 33 × 28; 1939. (The footstone similarly done but by another hand, 1965.)

737A/P Hopton-Wood stone wall tablet in the 'Little church' of Ealing Green church, London, w.5 in memory of WILTON EDWIN RIX, Minister of the church 1922–1939.

> At the foot in italic 'In Christo'.
> 21 × 14; 1939. (See also 403A/P)

738 Headstone in memory of MARY LETITIA OGSTON wife of Sir Herbert Grierson, 1868–1937.

> 30 × 41; 1939.

739 Headstone of Delabole slate in memory of Dr PERCY WALTER WHITE, 1874–1938, in the churchyard St Genesius, St Gennys, Bude, N. Cornwall.

> Killed by a fall of rock at Trebarwith Strand, near Tintagel. At the foot is a lovely 16 in. spray of E.G.'s leaves.
> R 25 × 18; 1939.

740 Foundation stone of Portland stone in the porch of Nottingham County Hall, laid by the Duke of Portland, 21 November 1939.

> The arms are in bas-relief with distinguished mantling in an oak leaf form and the motto 'Sapienter proficiens' tucked round the feet of the supporters. The inscription, well spaced out, is in fifteen lines. Architect, E. Vincent Harris.
> c.36 × 48; 1939.

741 Tablet of Delabole slate in Memorial Chapel, Rockingham, near Market Harborough, Leicestershire, in memory of LAVINIA, wife of BARON von ROEDER, 1853–1933, younger daughter of the Hon. Richard Watson.

> 'Be thou faithful unto death' in italic at the foot.
> R 13 × 20; 1939.

742 Headstone in memory of EDWARD ORFORD CAPON, d.1939, aged 65.

> 1939.

742A/P Letters over doors to staircases, Chapel Court, St John's College, Cambridge. Architect, Sir Edward Maufe.

> 1939.

742B/P Headstone in the Jewish Cemetery, Golders Green, London, N.W.11, of LINA RUBINSTEIN, 1889–1929.

> Seven lines of caps widely spaced. 1939.

743 Portland head- and footstone stated in the *Inventory* as being in the cemetery at Wellington, Somerset, in memory of JOHN WESLEY CLIFT, 1858–1939.

> 42 × 30; 1939.

744 Portland headstone on plinth with shield in relief (with motto ribbons below and above) and kerbing in Horson Cemetery, Torpoint, Plymouth, in memory of EVA MARGARET SANDEMAN, killed at Seaton.

> The work was executed in 1942 by David Kindersley from drawings made by E.G. in January 1940.

THIS
STON
BY H
DUKE
K.G.P
ON T

SAPIENTER PROFICIENS

21st DAY OF NO

THE YEAR OF OU

66   Detail of a rubbing of the foundation stone for Nottingham County Hall, 1939 (740).

745 Oak panel with coloured shield and inscription within the panelling on the west wall of Blundell's School Chapel, Tiverton, Devon, in memory of HUGH LEWIS OWEN, 1882–1938. Sarawak service 1921–29.

Nine lines of caps.
12 × 15; 1940.

746 Ledger of Portland stone in Newick churchyard, Sussex, in memory of the architect, GERALD MORLEY HORDER, 'who passed into the eternal', 1939.

Above the twelve-line spaciously arranged inscription is a dove within a thorny wreath in bas-relief. 1939.

747 Tablet of Hopton-Wood stone, on a wall opposite the Trout Inn, Godstow, Oxford, commemorating acquisition of land by the Oxford Preservation Trust, in 1934, through a gift by Philip Leslie Agnew, in memory of his son EWAN SIEGFRIED AGNEW, a student at New College, Oxford, 1912–1914.

R 19 × 31; 1940.

748 Portland headstone and kerbs in Ewhurst Churchyard, Surrey, in memory of PAUL LAUDER, 1880–1939.

1940.

748A Table-stone paperweight with inscription: THE SOULS OF THE RIGHTEOUS ARE IN THE HAND OF GOD & THERE SHALL NO TORMENT TOUCH THEM commissioned by Wilma, Lady Cawdor.

R 4 × 2; 1940.

748B/P Shield, with three figures, flanked by scallop shells, and motto: EX FORTI DVLCEDO, at Buxted, Sussex, for the house of Sir Edward Maufe.

c.1939.

749 Ledgerstone in East Sheen Cemetery, Mortlake, London, s.w.14, in memory of CHARLES FREDERICK KEARLEY.

1940.

749A/P Points of the compass, 'N.S.E. and W., 1940' incised on a floor at Pigotts, within a square frame.

9 × 9; 1940.

750 Blue Hornton stone in the garden of Baroda House, Kensington Palace Gardens, inscribed: 'HEATHER My constant companion and friend. Beloved by all. B. July 30th 1928, D. Feby. 26th 1940.' Commissioned by Sir Sydney Cockerell, on behalf of Mrs Chester Beatty, for the grave of her dog.

R 22 × 30; 1940.

751 Cruciform headstone of Portland stone at Box, nr Chippenham, Wilts., in memory of PATRICIA MARY LEVINGE, d.1940, aged 5 months.

R 15 × 15; 1940.

752 Portland ledgerstone in Stonefall Cemetery, Harrogate, in memory of TERESA MARY KELLY, d.1938.

Eight lines widely spaced below a large bas-relief cross: 'Blessed are the meek for they shall possess the land .. steel true, blade straight, R.I.P.' 1940.

753 Ledgerstone of Blue Hornton stone, in churchyard of St Lawrence, South Hinksey, Oxon., in memory of DAVID DUNCAN BADEN-POWELL, d.1939.

R 54 × 20; 1940.

754 Tablet of Portland stone on a wall in the garden of Sir Winston Churchill's house Chartwell, Westerham, Kent. This records: THE GREATER PART OF THIS / WALL WAS BUILT BETWEEN / THE YEARS / 1925 & 1932 / BY WINSTON WITH HIS OWN / HANDS. Commissioned by Lady Churchill.

R 30 × 18; 1940. (See also 754A)

754A Inscription on sundial in the garden of Sir Winston Churchill's house, Chartwell, Westerham, Kent, commissioned by Lady Churchill:

HERE LIES THE BALI DOVE.
IT DOES NOT DO TO WANDER
TOO FAR FROM SOBER MEN,
BUT THERE'S AN ISLAND YONDER –
I THINK OF IT AGAIN.

1940. (See also 754)

755 Headstone of Hopton-Wood stone, in Daviot Churchyard, Highland Region, in memory of VINCENT CARTWRIGHT VICKERS, 1878–1939, father of Wilma, Lady Cawdor.

R 22 × 13; 1940.

755A Headstone of Hopton-Wood stone, in Daviot Churchyard, Highland Region, in memory of ANTONY ALBERT VICKERS, 1913–1939, elder son of Vincent Cartwright Vickers, (a half brother of Wilma, Lady Cawdor).

R 28 × 13; 1940.

756 Hornton stone headstone in Apperley churchyard, Glos., in memory of ALGERNON STRICKLAND, 1891–1939.

He was the son-in-law of the Countess of Wemyss (cf 381 etc.). 1940.

757 Hopton-Wood stone tablet, St Peter's, Dumbleton, Evesham, in memory of COLLINS ASHWIN, Rector of Dumbleton, 1904–1938.

R 16 × 16; 1940.

758 Portland head- and footstone in Leamington Cemetery in memory of EDITH EIRENE CHAMBERS, 1865–1940.

1940.

759 Gravestone, St Mary and St John Baptist, Newtown, Newbury, Berks., in memory of SYBIL MARY WENTWORTH ROSKILL, 1871–1931, and of JOHN ROSKILL, 1860–1940.

> Eleven lines centred: cut by Laurie Cribb on an existing stone. A note in E.G.'s diary under 13th October, 1940 reads: 'Enthoven (the architect) inscription sketch in afternoon.' This was the last entry he made in his diary prior to entering Harefield Hospital, whither he went 1 November, and where he died 17 November 1940.

760 Headstone at Alnwick, Northumberland, in memory of LYDIA KATE ARMSTRONG, 1867–1940.

760A/P Inscriptions on the Hopton-Wood stone reredos in the Chapel of the English Martyrs, Westminster Cathedral. Beside the bas-relief figure of St Thomas More: TE MARTYRUM CANDIDATUS LAUDAT EXERCITUS, and St John Fisher: TU REX GLORIAE CHRISTI.

> The roman caps are arranged vertically; the left-hand inscription in two lines has an unexpected space below, due to the removal of the pet monkey on the order of Cardinal Griffin; a faint scar on St Thomas More's gown is all the evidence remaining. On the book he holds is CAESARIS CAESAR ET QUAE SUNT DEI DEO. Above the crucifix between the angels is a vigorously curved ribbon.
>
> The carving, begun by E.G., was completed after his death.

761 Crucifixion. A carving on sycamore wood with incised inscription: ET ANTE QVAM ME IN VOCETIS, DI CAM: ECCE ADSVM.

> This carving (11 × 8) was incised by Denis Tegetmeier after a drawing by E.G. It was in the collection of S. Samuels, Liverpool; now in the University of Texas at Austin. It seems to be E.G.'s 'V'-cut farewell: AND BEFORE YOU MAY CALL ME I SHALL SAY, BEHOLD, HERE I AM ... 1940.

762 Head- and footstones in the cemetery at Speen, Bucks., in memory of Eric Gill, born 22 February 1882, died 17 November 1940. The inscription, surmounted by a cross, reads: PRAY FOR ME / ERIC GILL / STONE CARVER / 1882–1940. Carved on the footstone is the device 'St Thomas's Hands' and 'Veritas' which E.G. used as an identifying symbol in many of the books he wrote. Designed by E.G. the inscription was cut by Laurie Cribb.

> Mary Gill's death was recorded later on the stone.
> R 15 × 19 and 8 × 7; 1940.

Two other memorials may here be recorded. The earlier one is a tablet let into the floor beneath the fourteenth Station of the Cross in Westminster Cathedral: E.G. / LAPIDARIUS / 1882–1940 / R.I.P. This was designed and cut by Laurie Cribb in 1942. The later one is a tablet in Portland stone affixed to the wall of 32 Hamilton Road, Brighton. The design follows that which E.G. drew for similar tablets affixed to houses in Brighton (cf 458). The inscription surmounted by a carving of dolphins, reads: ERIC GILL / STONE CARVER / WAS BORN IN THIS / HOUSE ON THE 22nd / FEBRUARY 1882 / 'Erected by the Regency Society'. This was drawn and cut by Joseph Cribb and fixed in September 1960.

Appendix I: Apprentices, Pupils or Assistants 1906–1940

(*Denotes Apprentices)

LONDON: 1906–8

CHRISTIE, Lawrence (1907–8)
*CRIBB, Herbert Joseph (1906–8)
GILL, Macdonald (1906–8)
STAPLETON, George (1906–7)

DITCHLING: 1907–24

BEEDHAM, Ralph J. (1917–24)
CHUTE, Desmond (1918–22)
CRIBB, Herbert Joseph (1907–24)
CRIBB, Laurence (1922–24)
*GEERING, S. (1914–15)
GILL, Macdonald (1907–24)
HAGREEN, Philip (1924–25)
JONES, David (1921–24)
*LEANEY, Albert (1914–21)
*STRATTON, Hilary (1920–21)
TEGETMEIER, Denis (1921)
TOMSETT, George (1914–20)
*WHITE, Frederick (1910–12)

CAPEL-Y-FFIN: 1924–28

ANSTED, René (1925–27)
CRIBB, Herbert Joseph (1924–28)
CRIBB, Laurence (1924–28)
JONES, David (1924–27)

PIGOTTS, HIGH WYCOMBE: 1928–40

BEYER, Ralph (1937–38)
CRIBB, Herbert Joseph (1928–34)
CRIBB, Laurence (1928–40)
FOSTER, Anthony (1933–40)
KINDERSLEY, David (1934–36)
LORIMER, Hew (1934–35)
MacDOUGALL, Angus (1934–36)
PELHAM, Prudence (1930–31)
POTTER, Donald (1931–32)
RICHEY, Michael (1936–39)
RITCHIE, Walter (1938–39)
SHARPE, John (1937)
*SKELTON, John (1940)
TEGETMEIER, Denis (1928–40)

NOTE: Eric Gill moved from London (Hammersmith) to Ditchling 12 September 1907 but retained a workshop at Hammersmith until 23 April 1908. The Capel-y-ffin period was from 13 August 1924 until 11 October 1928 when he moved to Pigotts. He died 17 November 1940.

Appendix II: Locations by Counties and Countries

NOTE: The Index of Locations needs to be consulted for entry numbers, some of which may have been destroyed. Some items in collections in the U.S.A. are not included.

COUNTIES OF ENGLAND

AVON
Bath
Bristol
Corston
Cotham
Easter Compton
Leigh Woods

BEDFORDSHIRE
Silsoe
Sutton

BERKSHIRE
Bisham
Brimpton
Newtown, Newbury
North Moreton
Radley
Stratfieldsaye
Upper Woolhampton
Waltham St Lawrence
Windsor
Winkfield

BUCKINGHAMSHIRE
Beaconsfield
Butler's Cross
Chorleywood
Eton
Great Brickhill
Great Missenden
Pigotts, High Wycombe
Langley Marish
Little Hampden
Speen
Stone
Stowe

CAMBRIDGESHIRE
Barton
Cambridge
Peterborough
Trumpington

CHESHIRE
Chester
Knutsford
Over Peover
Over Tabley
Thelwall

CORNWALL
Bude
Pelynt, Looe
St Gennys

CUMBRIA
Carlisle
Reckerby

DERBYSHIRE
Ashbourne

DEVON
Chevithorn
Clovelly
Exeter
Plymouth
Tiverton
Torbay
Torpoint
Torquay

DORSET
Affpuddle

Bradpole
Bridport
Cranbourne
Lulworth Cove
Parkstone
Tarrant Keynston
Tolpuddle

CO DURHAM
Bournmoor

ESSEX
Clacton-on-Sea
Colchester
Dunmow
Gilston
Great Waltham
Great Warley
Harlow
Romford
Upminster
Woodford Green

GLOUCESTERSHIRE
Apperley
Bourton-on-the-Hill
Cheltenham
Didbrook
Ebrington
Little Compton
Painswick
Stanway
Weston-sub-Edge

HAMPSHIRE
Bournemouth
Bransgore

Burley
Holdenhurst
Liss
Portsmouth
Sennicotts
Sopley
Southampton
Sutton Scotney
Winchester
Wonston

HEREFORDSHIRE
Belmont Abbey
Broxwood

HERTFORDSHIRE
Bayford
Bushey
Hatfield
Letchworth
Watford

ISLE OF WIGHT
Ryde

KENT
Betteshanger
Birchington
Canterbury
Charlton
Chartwell
Chelsfield
Ham
Horsmonden
Hythe
Lee
Lympne

Salisbury
Stourton
Teffont Evias
Wilsford
Wilton

WORCESTERSHIRE
Broadway
Burlingham
Dumbleton
Evesham
Hagley
Hook
Malvern
Norton
Tenbury Wells
Upton-on-Severn

YORKSHIRE
Armley, Leeds
Bradford
Burnsall
Cloughton
Escrick
Gilling East
Harrogate
Ilkley
Leeds
Mirfield
Northallerton
Pickering
Richmond

Scarborough
Selby
Skipton
Whitby
Wykeham Abbey
York

COUNTIES OF
WALES

CLWYD
Chirk
Clocaenog

DYFED
Caldey Island
Llandyfaelog
Tenby

GLAMORGAN
Cardiff

GWENT
Capel-y-ffin
Llanvaches
Llanwenarth Citra
Newport
Tredunnoc

GWYNEDD
Pentrefoelas
Tudweiliog

REGIONS OF
SCOTLAND

GRAMPIAN
Aberdeen
Banchory
Drumoak
Logie Coldstone

HIGHLAND
Daviot
Kingussie

STRATHCLYDE
Coatbridge
Glasgow
Knockdolian

TAYSIDE
Broughty Ferry

COUNTRIES

ALBANIA
Tirana

AUSTRALIA
Adelaide
Melbourne

FRANCE
Amiens
Boulogne
Cambrai
Clerment Ferrand
Paris

INDIA
Jagdalpur
Nagur

IRELAND
Donegal

ISRAEL
Jerusalem

PAPUA NEW GUINEA
Rogoa Island, Samarai

SOUTH AFRICA
Cape Town

SWITZERLAND
Geneva
Suhr bei Aarau

USA
Austin, Texas
Cambridge, Massachusetts

ZAMBIA
Lusaka

Appendix III: War Memorials

Eric Gill designed thirty-eight war memorials, all but two for World War I. The first, dating from 1901, was for a cloister at Charterhouse School in gothic style for those who died in the South African war of 1899–1901. This was probably the first draughtsman's job Gill was engaged on in W. D. Caröe's office. The lettering is Lombardic. Though this was a form of letter he soon grew out of, under the influence of Edward Johnston, the foundation stone and its associated stones and lettering on the buttress are so integral with the design of the building that they give an early indication of that unity of stone and architecture which was characteristic of Gill's later work.

The first Gill memorial of World War I was designed as early as 1915: a large crucifix for a prominent road junction at Bisham, Berkshire. Several are at such junctions: Chirk in North Wales (359), Stanway in the Cotswolds (381), Dunmow in Essex (397), and one of the most impressive at Affpuddle in Dorset (347). This 25-ft-high monument bears just five names. In contrast, there are 1,260 on two 30-ft-wide walls at Islington (437).

As the best-known letter cutter of his day Gill was commissioned to carve the war memorials at the British Museum and the Victoria and Albert Museum – in both cases, as at Charterhouse, showing a perfect response to the architectural site. Town and village churches all over the country from Sussex to Yorkshire have small and distinguished memorials, where often their simplicity belies the skill in siting and the layout of the lettering. Inside churches certain words are gilded, and red and blue are used in the 'V'-cut letters. There are also countless wall tablets to individuals fallen in World War I – some of which have still to be located. In these and general memorials the choice of commemorative words is often unusual to our present thinking, and thus evocative of that era and its countless tragedies: 'fighting in the Great War against the Germans' (314); 'For a tomb they have an altar, for lamentation memory, and for pity praise' (381); 'A stone of remembrance from the soil of France' (401).

A list of E.G.'s war memorials in towns and villages, universities, schools and colleges is given below.

SOUTH AFRICAN WAR	WORLD WAR I
3 Charterhouse	*337 Bisham, Berks.
15 Canterbury (now covered)	*347 Affpuddle, Dorset

Appendix IV: Heraldry

Though Eric Gill is understood to have had a low opinion of heraldry, there is no doubt that he understood the art of it. His work reflected the essentials of medieval designs – good shield shapes, charges designed boldly and filling the spaces well – and was doubtless influenced by W. R. Lethaby and the book which appeared under his editorship in 1913, *Heraldry for Craftsmen and Designers* by Sir William St John Hope. This comprehensive look at the origins of heraldry, and its treatment on seals, monuments, buildings, and in many materials, showed the flexibility of heraldic design within the canons of its disciplines; and flexibility is especially echoed in Gill's heraldry, notably in his treatment of mantling.

The element of a full coat of arms termed mantling is that which flows out from either side of a helm below the crest, originally only a simple cloth, much elaborated in successive periods as a decorative feature. Gill's mantlings were diverse and free in treatment, as also were the motto ribbons which were usually associated with the designs. He had no standard form for the ribbon, as was adopted by many other designers; like his mantlings his mottoes flow with a characteristic verve, and the length of the words help to determine the design.

The list of forty-nine designs given below, alas excludes one of his finest because it lacks lettering – in Chapel Court, St John's College, Cambridge. The designs range in scale (from 4 ft high to a 1½-in. shield at Eton). The earliest, that of Archbishop Frederick Temple shows Caröe's Lombardic influence at its most severe, but before long Gill developed a style of his own – at Stone, near Aylesbury, with its spiky, holly-leaf mantling, and at St Paul's where Holman Hunt's arms are fitted elegantly into a circle. For the nobility, his achievements for Wellesley at Stratfieldsaye, and the Herbert tomb in the private graveyard in Wilton Park are very distinguished. Bentalls' arms on the great store at Kingston upon Thames can be enjoyed from the street, others in churches and colleges.

The list of coats of arms or crests, and some regimental badges associated with the inscriptions, is given below. Arms evidently by Caröe within a baroque cartouche or a strapwork surround are not included.

44 Temple, Canterbury

48 Great Ormond Street Hospital, London

96 Lawley, Escrick, Yorks.

97 Manners, Thorney Hill, Bransgore, Hants

103 Townshend, site unknown

*110 Smyth, Stone, nr Aylesbury

121 Lovelace, Ockham, Surrey

157 Langford-Brooke, Over Tabley, Cheshire (crest only)

165 Eton College (Warre)

218 Regimental badges, Bournemouth

*221 Holman Hunt, St Paul's, London

267 Rich, Calne, Wilts.

268 Aylwin, Sevenoaks

282 O'Neill, Lincoln Cathedral

*314 Wellesley, Stratfieldsaye, Berks.

324 Lyttleton, Hagley, Worcs.

325 Calthrop, nr Malvern (?)

344 Kelly, Eton College (crest only)

358A/P Conyngham

372 Gough, Winchester Cathedral

383 Fitzgerald, Eton College

*389 New Zealand, Thorney Hill, Bransgore, Hants

399A/P Sherwood Foresters, and Notts. and Derby Regt, Ashbourne, Derbyshire

416 Treherne, Mayfield, Sussex

426 Lindley, East Carlton, Northants.

441 Manwood (?), Sandwich, Kent

*478 Herbert, Brushford, Somerset

480 Ellesmere College, Shropshire

485 Heathcoat Amory (crest only)

508 Fernandes, site unknown (3 shields)

543 Hamersley, Pyrton, Oxon.

554 Fanshawe, site unknown

570 Middleton, site unknown

572A/P White-Thomson, Jesus College, Cambridge

*580 Rushout, Burford, Shropshire

608 Radcliffe Library, Oxford (3 shields)

611 Coplestone, Handbridge, Chester

*633 Bentalls, Kingston upon Thames, Surrey

637 Wignall, site unknown

651 Carter memorial, St Mary's, Hackney Wick (5 shields)

652 St Clair Donaldson memorial, Hackney Wick (4 shields)

658 Madden, St Paul's, London

678 Leicester, Holkham, Norfolk

685 Black Watch badge, Jerusalem

691 Heathcoat Amory, Chevithorne, Devon

*708 Herbert, Wilton, Wilts.

726 Benckendorff, Westminster Cathedral

*740 Nottingham County Council, Nottingham

744 Sandeman, Torpoint, Devon

745 Owen, Blundell's School, Tiverton, Devon

748B/P Maufe, Buxted, Sussex

Appendix V: Designs for Seals, Medals and Coins

SEALS

Gill's work on seals began early in his career. In 1905 he designed a seal for the University College Transfer Commissioners (who were responsible for 'incorporating' the College into the University of London, where, twenty-eight years later, Gill carved the foundation stone (594) for Senate House). This seal has closely crowded lines of roman caps similar to the inscription over the door of Westcott House in Cambridge (41), cut in 1904. Other seals were designed for the King's College Transfer Commissioners and the Irish Sailors and Soldiers Land Trust.

Gill was invited to submit designs for the Great Seal of King George V, but none was carried out. Three designs, of 1914 and 1929, deserve to be illustrated here, and show what we have lost. Whether the 1929 design with its three rings of lettering was submitted 'tongue in cheek' is not known, but it falls within Gill's practice of having fun when he could.

MEDALS

In 1923 the *Daily Herald* commissioned Gill to design a bronze medal for the Order of Industrial Heroism. It was inaugurated by the newspaper as an award for outstanding bravery in mines or workshops, or by railwaymen, dockers, seamen and other industrial workers. Recommendations for awards were made by the Trades Union Congress, or by a union.

The medal was not made by the Mint, but by George Friend who had engraved many metal tablets for Gill. Friend's assistants, Turner and Kavenagh, engraved the reverse lettering. On the obverse the letters O I H are simply placed beside a relief of St Christopher. On the reverse the letters are skilfully arranged round a small circle; and as so often in Gill's work, three sizes of letter are used. The space at the foot was for the name of the recipient.

This 'worker's VC', with an illuminated certificate (£10 was added later as a gratuity), was awarded to 378 workers or groups. It ran for forty years until 1964, when the *Daily Herald* was succeeded by the *Sun*.

Other medals were engraved by Friend, and designed by Gill: one with lettering only commemorating George V; one with a bas-relief of the Deposition and EASTER, and another relief engraved: ERIC GILL O S D with a portrait.

Another medal commission came from Gill's reputation for bas-relief sculpture. He was invited to design a medal to be struck by the Royal Mint for J.S. Fry and Sons Ltd, to mark the firm's bicentenary in 1928. His design was not accepted, but deserves illustrating here.

67　The Order of Industrial Heroism, 1923.

68　Seal of the University College Transfer
Commissioners, 1905.

69 Boxwood carving for a proposed commemorative medal for J. S. Fry & Sons, 4 × 4, c.1927.

70   Sketch designs for the Great Seal of King George V, 1914 (above) and 1929 (opposite).

71 *Some rare signatures.*

COINS

In 1924, at the request of the Royal Mint, Gill made a series of drawings for a new set of silver coins. In his letters (nos 120 and 122) he mentions that others had also been approached, and that he 'should have a go at it'. Heraldry and St George were to be abandoned in favour of new symbols. In his methodical way he studied British coins in the British Museum, and thought the silver pennies of King Offa of Mercia from about AD 800 the most beautiful. Two of his completed designs bore the cross with four dots used as a kind of signature in his early days.

In the event, Gill's designs, though well considered by the Mint, were not used; but two are recorded here since they certainly come within the definition of inscriptional work. Some of the sketches echo the bold original division of words sometimes adopted in his gravestones, for example: ONE / FLO / RIN / 1924 divided by the arms of a cross; HA / LF / CRO / WN and even O / NEC / ROW / N. Somehow I feel these were his undoing in the eyes of officialdom.

Neither a symbolic bas-relief of belching chimneys for the half-crown coin, nor the ear of wheat, a theme used by coin makers in ancient Greece, found favour. A report by the Deputy Master and Comptroller of the Mint for 1927 stated that Mr Gill 'works in a style which is definitely archaic. By so doing, however, he deliberately debars himself from employment in the designing of many medals which do not lend themselves to his very special style ... Still less is Mr Gill's work suited to modern coinage design.' The report goes on to regret that 'except on very special occasions, the Royal Mint is by force of circumstances precluded from utilising the skill and indeed the genius, of so fine an artist and so definitely outstanding a craftsman'.

In the end, though never issued as coinage, the only designs by Gill for which specimens were made by the Mint were the shilling, the sixpence, and the threepenny bit.

Appendix VI: Postage Stamps

Eric Gill's reputation for fine lettering and engraving brought him to the forefront of industrial design, reflected in his election as one of the first Royal Designers for Industry; and he was one of many eminent designers and engravers to be given the challenging job of designing postage stamps.

This is not the place to describe all the designs and changes of detail required by the Post Office in consultation with the Royal Fine Art Commission and the King. Indeed, one of these, for the British Empire Exhibition at Wembley in 1924, resulted in a note: 'The King cannot think Mr Gill's 1½d design at all attractive …'

Gill's contribution to the stamps for the brief reign of Edward VIII in 1936 was the use of Gill Sans type for the word POSTAGE and the denomination of the stamp, in accordance with the simplicity wanted by the King. The effect was mean, uncharacteristic of Gill. In contrast, the stamps which he designed for the reign of George VI, and in use 1937–47, were distinguished and remarkably restrained, with roman caps simply used to balance POSTAGE and REVENUE beside Edmund Dulac's head of the King. The corners of the various issues were typical Gill treatments, heraldic in nature, including a rose, thistle, daffodil, shamrock, lions, a dragon, and a harp.

Two other designs deserve special mention: the GPO 'logo' used 1934–54, and the design for the Stamp Centenary issue in 1940. The latter bore a gull with a typically well-drawn ribbon in its beak with the dates, echoing Gill's genius for heraldic motto ribbons.

72   *Postage stamp: George VI, 1937.*   73   *Postage stamp: Post centenary, 1940.*

Appendix VII: Alphabets

Outline drawing of 2½ in. letters designed for cutting in stone, 1903, 20A

Roman capitals incised with 'V' section, 1909, 168A

Lower case italics and numerals incised with 'V' section, 1909, 168B

Raised capitals and numerals, 1909, 168C

Wood letters in 1½ in. roman capitals, c.1916, 331A

Capital letters incised on stone, 1927, 498

Capital letters in relief on stone, 1927, 498A

Roman capitals, lower-case letters and numerals incised on stone, 1932, 585A, 668

Alphabets and numerals, italic with flourished caps, for the Worshipful Company of Goldsmiths, 1934, 612A/P

Outline drawing for incised 2 in. letters with numerals, 1938, 706A

An alphabet carved for Sculpture and Memorials Co., 1938, 711

Roman capitals and lower-case letters with Arabic numerals and an inscription: 'Felix qui potuit' … 1939, 732A

Roman capitals and lower-case letters with numerals incised on stone, 1939, 732B, 732C, 732D

Appendix VIII: Unidentified inscriptions

There are eighteen rubbings of inscriptions in the St Bride Printing Library which, for a variety of reasons, Evan Gill did not include in the Inventory. They are now listed here. The Library also holds many drawings for work which was not carried out, but these are not included.

U1 ST JOSEPH'S COTTAGE & ST PETER'S.

    Six lines of caps, and emblems of a lily and keys.
    R 33 × 16; 1920.

U2 Portland gravestone, executed but not erected, for DIANA SUTTON 1915–1926.

    Seven lines of caps, and AD DEUM QUI LAETIFICAVIT JUVENTUTUM MEAM.
    R 24 × 20.

U3 THE FIRST INSCRIPTION OF HILARY STRATTON SUSSEX 1920.

U4 LUDWIG MOND F.R.S.

    At Cambridge.
    R 8 × 6.

U5 Details for a poster 80 × 30: 'ENO'S FRUIT SALT First thing every morning' for Gerald Meynell, 1929.

U6 NOT APOLLO, NOT DIONYSOS BUT APOLLO AND DIONYSOS.

    Two lines of caps with two kinds of 'Y'.
    R 16 × 10.

U7 IN HOC COGNOVIMUS … on facets of an eight-sided stone 8 in. deep. Half-inch caps in two lines.

U8 GOD LEADETH: IT IS WELL.

    4 in. uncial caps of great authority 'V'-cut on an oak beam.
    R 78 × 6.

U9 ALL SAINTS CHURCH in relief within a recessed panel, in similar vein to U8.

    R 30 × 3.

U10 DEI PAX IN HAC DOMO SIT.

    Three lines of caps, the 'P' very long.
    R 18 × 17.

U11 CHRIST SAID HE THAT BELIEVETH IN ME HATH EVERLASTING LIFE.

Five lines of caps.
R 18 × 16; probably c.1906.

U12 & STILL A GARDEN BY THE WATER BLOWS on a square tablet arranged
diamondwise.

Five lines, with THE joined.
R 10 × 10; probably c.1906.

U13 HE LOVED TO SEEK PEACE AND ENSUE IT: HE LOVED JUSTICE & EQUITY
& RIGHTEOUSNESS: HE SHOWED HIMSELF GENTLE & MERCIFUL FOR
CHRIST'S SAKE.

Five lines.
R 30 × 10.

U14 THE LORD THY GOD / Dominum Deum tuum / SHALT THOU ADORE /
adorabis et illi soli servies / AND HIM ONLY / SHALT THOU SERVE.

The caps interspersed with italic.
R 15 × 13.

U15 DEAR RAMSAY 13 July 1940, on an elliptical-headed stone. Probably for a dog's
grave.

R 16 × 10.

U16 AGNUS DEI QUI TOLLIS ... REQUIEM.

R 6 × 4.

U17 CARITAS NUNQUAM EXCIDIT ... CARITAS.

R 25 × 15.

U18 HIC ES ET HIC MANETO.

R c.3 × 2.

Select Bibliography

NOTE: The literature on Gill is extensive and covered in other publications. The aim here is to list seminal works and some of those more related to his inscriptional work.

ERIC GILL, 'Inscriptions in Stone' in *Writing & Illuminating & Lettering* by Edward Johnston, John Hogg, London, 1906.

ROBERT HARLING, *The Letter Forms and Type Designs of Eric Gill*, Westerham Press, 1976.

DAVID RUTT, 'Eric Gill, stamp designer manqué', *Typos 5*, London College of Printing, 1982.

FIONA MacCARTHY, *Eric Gill*, Faber and Faber, London, 1989.

CHRISTOPHER SKELTON (ed.), *Eric Gill: The Engravings*, The Herbert Press, London, 1990 (first published as a limited edition, *The Engravings of Eric Gill*, by Christopher Skelton, 1983).

SEBASTIAN CARTER (ed.), 'Eric Gill: the continuing tradition', *Monotype Recorder*, 1990.

DAVID KINDERSLEY, *Mr Eric Gill: Further Thoughts by an Apprentice*, Cardozo Kindersley Editions, Cambridge, 1990.

EVAN GILL, *Eric Gill: A Bibliography*, 2nd edn revised by D. Steven Corey and Julia MacKenzie, St Paul's Bibliographies, Winchester, 1991.

DAVID PEACE, *Addenda and Corrigenda to the Inscriptional Work of Eric Gill*, Brick Row Bookshop, San Francisco, 1972.

– 'Eric Gill: a continuing influence', *Churchscape*, No. 4, 1985, pp. 30–36.

– *Glass Engraving: Lettering and Design* (section on Eric Gill), Batsford, London, 1985.

– 'The Stations of the Cross' in two parts; 'An Altarpiece', Westminster Cathedral Newsletter, 1985–88.

– 'The lettering at Christ Church, Brixton', *Church Building*, 1985.

Index of Persons and Institutions

Capitals denote persons commemorated.
Names in lower-case type relate to persons or institutions who either commissioned the work or have it in their keeping.

Index of Locations